W9-AFG-210

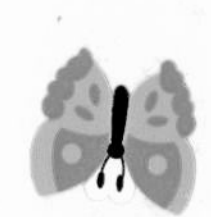

The Watcher at the Nest

4M Proclaims Territory

The Watcher at the Nest

by

MARGARET MORSE NICE

Illustrated by

ROGER TORY PETERSON

DOVER PUBLICATIONS, INC.

NEW YORK

Published in Canada by General Publishing Company, Ltd., 30 Lesmill Road, Don Mills, Toronto, Ontario.
Published in the United Kingdom by Constable and Company, Ltd., 10 Orange Street, London WC 2.

This Dover edition, first published in 1967, is an unabridged republication with minor corrections of the work first published by the Macmillan Company in 1939.

Library of Congress Catalog Card Number: 66-29059

Manufactured in the United States of America
Dover Publications, Inc.
180 Varick Street
New York, N.Y. 10014

To Three

Who Have Helped

With This Book

CONSTANCE NICE

KATHARINE MORSE

WILLIAM VOGT

CONTENTS

THE WATCHER AT THE NEST

CHAPTER 1

The Way of a Song Sparrow

IT WAS the rose hedge that formed the boundary between the domains of the two Song Sparrows that shared our garden. Uno claimed all the land around the house, the steep bluff directly west of it, and the three Norway maples in the garden proper, while 4M was owner of the ground beyond, starting with the hedge and including a box elder and a great silver maple on a meadow of blue grass. That this ownership was no mere figure of speech will be evident in the course of the narrative; the land was defended and won by age-old ceremonies and fierce battle, as definitely as in our courts of law, a piece of ground being released and quitclaimed by one bird and lawfully seized by the other.

These two birds, Uno and 4M, are the heroes of my story. Their conflicts with each other and their other neighbors, their luck with their wives and devotion to their babies, the exuberance of their glorious singing—not to mention the fortunes of their sons and daughters, grandchildren and great-grandchildren—all these were watched season in and season out until tragedy overtook them. Uno lived in our garden for three years, while 4M by the greatest good fortune escaped the perils that beset his kind for nearly three times as long. Uno was my first love among the Song Sparrows, but 4M, because of his long life and notable character, was to become, as an eminent German ornithologist put it, "world-famous."

It might be well to remind those of my readers who are not bird students that the Song Sparrow in no way—except in size—resembles the familiar, yet alien, English Sparrow. The two differ in plumage, voice, and manners, and, indeed, belong to distinct families. The Song Sparrow's colors are brown and grey; back and breast are heavily streaked, and in the middle of the breast there is a characteristic dark spot.

When in the fall of 1927 we came to Columbus, Ohio, we settled near the banks of the Olentangy because of the great weed tangle that stretched between our house and the river. The sixty acres of land which I called Interpont offered a bit of wilderness to the birds and me. Great cottonwoods and sycamores lined the banks of the stream, while a row of elms and hackberries had sprung up along an old fence. Patches of elders stood white in the late spring, and a deserted vineyard was overrun with briars. Weeds were everywhere—jungles of giant ragweed along the dikes that led to the river and along its sides, inhospitable nettles in the shade of the cottonwoods, thickets of burdocks, spectacular cow parsnips, and hosts of others. In short, Interpont was a tangled waste, despised by the conventional, but a place of happiness to the boys of the neighborhood, carp fishermen, an ornithologist, and the wild creatures.

It was on March 26, 1928, that I made an important capture in my trap on the feeding shelf—the first Song Sparrow that I had ever banded. Later I was glad to note that he had taken up his territory next to us. I called him Uno, while the male nesting to the south was 2M, the one to the north 3M, and the bird to the west 4M. The last-named individual attracted my attention by his fine and varied singing, and four of his songs I recorded in my notebook.

One morning a robbery occurred in our garden. I was sitting quietly near the north rosebush when a male Cowbird alighted on the woodshed, giving his high double note; a minute later, much to the distress of a Field Sparrow and a pair of Indigo Buntings, a female appeared. She vanished into the weeds and shortly returned, carrying in her bill an egg which she leisurely ate, contents and shell, while poor 4M and his mate protested.

A few days later I found Uno's nest well concealed under a large dandelion on the bluff. When the eggs hatched, I settled down to watch the parents, Uno being distinguished by a band on each leg, and his mate by a dark crescent on her side, evidently the result of some injury. She was an efficient mother, knowing exactly what to do with babies, for, although she had the task of brooding them, she fed them more often than Uno did during the first two days. This may well have been his first experience with fatherhood. He soon woke up to his responsibilities, however, and outdid his mate not only in the number of meals brought, but particularly in their size, for some of the insects he carried looked nearly as large as his offspring.

Unfortunately some predator carried off Uno's babies. 4M had even worse luck, for he lost not only his nest but his mate as well. We left Columbus in early June and knew nothing further of the happenings in our garden that season.

To my unbounded delight Uno entered my trap on March 9, 1929, giving me 100 per cent "return" for this species. My return percentages with Song Sparrows have always been high, but never again did they reach perfection.

To those of my readers who have not heard of the great game of bird banding let me briefly explain that hundreds of thousands of birds each year in Europe, India, Japan, and North America are being provided with aluminum anklets, each bearing a number and an address to which a report should be made in case the bird is found. In our country it is the United States Biological Survey that supplies the bands and serves as the clearing house. Many of the birds are banded as nestlings, but others are adults, captured in a variety of traps that lure the subjects within by means of bait, and take them unharmed by tripping devices, funnels, or the pulling of a string by the eager watcher. So little does the experience of banding seem to frighten most birds that some enter the traps many times a day. This is called "repeating"; "return" is used in connection with the recapture of a bird at or near the place of banding after a migration.

The object of banding is to individualize the birds, to enable one to know he is observing a particular subject and not another that looks just like him. Aluminum bands have afforded rich stores of information on migration, even though recoveries of marked birds do not ordinarily run above three to four per cent. For life-history studies, however, colored celluloid rings need to be used in addition to the official band of aluminum, for by means of different colors and different arrangements a large number of birds can be individually marked and readily distinguished in the wild with the aid of field glasses. Some students glue colored feathers to the tails of their subjects, but I feared that such conspicuous badges might jeopardize my birds.

Although Uno received the warmest of welcomes from me, the situation was vastly different in the garden. Ever since February 26th I had been studying with great interest 4M's splendid singing from the big silver maple in the west end of our land and the box elder in the middle of the garden. But on the day of Uno's capture I noted:

"4M is spreading himself over two territories and seems to take special delight today in singing right next to our house, over land that belonged to Uno last year. Poor Uno—he always was a mild-mannered Song Sparrow. I don't know what he will do."

Early the next morning I found out. I quote from my notebook:

4M and Uno Dispute Boundaries

"Uno and 4M are in Uno's southeast corner, down on the ground and in the weeds; Uno sings quite steadily from these low positions—rapidly and not loudly. They pay no attention to me, although I am very near. Both are very much puffed out, and even fly in this odd shape. 4M says nothing, but follows Uno, going for him or after him every minute or so, but not fiercely; Uno merely flies a few feet. This keeps up for perhaps ten minutes. Then 4M grows more belligerent, chases Uno around and about, and at last they come to blows, falling to the ground and fighting furiously. They separate and Uno sings in the Norway maple, while 4M goes to his box elder. Each sings and sings and sings."

Apparently the battle is won and the territory apportioned.

The witnessing of this "territory establishment" sealed my fate for the next seven years. I was so fascinated by this glimpse behind the scenes with my Song Sparrows, that I then and there determined to watch Uno for several hours every day, so as to follow the daily course of his life, to find out the meaning of his notes and postures, in short, to discover exactly what he did and how he did it. In particular I wanted to study the matter of "territory," which has been a burning question with ornithologists ever since the appearance of H. Eliot Howard's *"Territory in Bird Life"* in England in 1920, although the basal facts had been pointed out fifty years earlier in Germany by Bernard Altum. "Territory," as Ernst Mayr defines it, "is an area occupied by one male of a species which it defends against intrusions of other males of the same species and in which it makes itself conspicuous." Although it was obvious, once it had been pointed out, that many birds were territorial, yet hardly a beginning had been made in determining details with various species.

Incredible as it may seem, almost complete ignorance reigned as to the life history of this abundant, friendly, and well-nigh universally distributed bird. I went to the books and read that this species has two notes besides the song, and that incubation lasted ten to fourteen days and was performed by both sexes—meager enough information and all of it wrong. The men at the State Museum, fine field naturalists and well acquainted with the local birds, could not answer my questions; they did not know whether 4M's singing in late February meant that he had taken up his territory, nor could they tell me when the nesting Song Sparrows arrived. None of us suspected that some of our breeding birds were permanently resident, for we believed that all our wintering Song Sparrows nested farther to the north. Indeed, I have never had a subject of research in which I had so little idea what to expect as these Song Sparrows. It was an unknown world, and each day I made fresh discoveries.

The main business of 4M and Uno at first was song. And what was its significance? Was it "a sweet and sincere little petition," a "little prayer of thankfulness" sent "straight up to heaven by the shortest route"? I fear we will have to discard this pious fancy. As Bernard Altum stated nearly seventy years ago, the song of a territorial bird at the beginning of the season is a warning and an invitation—in short, an advertisement that this particular bit of land is preempted by a certain male, that other males must keep their distance, but that a mate will be heartily welcomed.

From dawn on through the morning each male spent most of his time on high points over his territory singing steadily at the rate of some seven songs a minute; the chief interruptions, besides brief meals, being sallies to clear the land of trespassers of his own or other species. By the middle of March the migration of transient Song Sparrows was in full swing and all owners of territories busied themselves chasing these unfortunate travelers. I thought a tourist camp was sorely needed.

I began to wonder how Uno would recognize a possible mate, since both sexes are dressed alike. And I looked forward eagerly to learning what form of courtship display and special song he would use to win the lady.

Then all at once both Song Sparrows stopped singing. Instead of two hundred and sixty songs an hour, perhaps three were given. The change was nothing short of startling. It seemed as if Uno *must* sing as he alighted on one favorite singing perch after another.

My notes at this time are full of puzzling situations as the following excerpts will show.

"Mar. 15. Uno approaches a new Song Sparrow; it flips its wings, then opens its bill and says *eee eee eee* in a high nasal tone. Uno retires; it flies into a small tree; Uno dashes for it and attacks it.

"Uno has a short fierce fight with a stranger, after which he stands with crest raised and bill open. Stranger doesn't leave. As if Uno didn't have troubles enough this morning, 4M is back again, hunched up, threatening him.

"Mar. 17. Uno flies down near the stranger; 4M appears in the shape of a balloon. Uno spreads out his tail, but little else. He always keeps between 4M and Stranger. Why *don't* Uno and 4M sing any more?

"Mar. 18. Uno hops on lawn, Stranger keeps behind. He goes up the road a way, is chased by some other Song Sparrow, tries to get back to his land, but is driven off by a cross scold from Stranger who is perched on the corner burdock. (Think this must have been a migrating male of considerable courage.) If Uno were not banded, I should be perfectly distracted by this multiplicity of birds that all look practically alike."

It was not until the next day that the truth began to dawn upon me. I noted: "Stranger starts working up the bank as if hunting for a nesting site; at one hollow she twitches her wings."

So Stranger was Uno's mate! But still I had seen no courting.

"I think I have solved the problem as to how males tell females," I wrote. "When the owner of the land dashes at a strange bird, a male either flees or fights; a female shouts *eee eee eee,* and he at once desists from any exhibition of hostility."

But Uno behaved very oddly at times.

"Una flies down from the south end, Uno rushes at her, hits her, and leaves singing triumphantly. She crouches there, saying *eee eee eee*. This must have been a mistake on Uno's part."

At length I realized that this "pouncing" *is* Song Sparrow courtship, that and the sudden cessation of song. Uno guarded Una from attentions of 4M and other males, and he gave the excited *tit tit tit tit* of fear when a cat or hawk appeared, thus showing his concern for her safety. And although he dominated her by his pouncing, yet in many little everyday encounters, *she* dominated *him,* and the net result was that they were the best of friends.

By the study and interpretation of my notes in the light of experience, I discovered that 4M's mate—Quarta—had arrived the day before Una did. The two pairs met many times a day at the feeding station I maintained on the boundary between the two territories. Sometimes my conscience pricked me about this arrangement; two feeding stations would have meant fewer quarrels, but how much less exciting life would have been! I will describe a meeting:

"4M balloons at Uno who is somewhat puffed up with tail spread. 4M goes near Quarta who pecks at him. Una balloons at Quarta who retires. Males threaten back and forth, coming within three inches of each other. Suddenly a real fight is staged, the males springing into the air, the females seizing each other with bill and claw, then an indiscriminate melee."

Perhaps two-thirds of the encounters passed off with mere bluffing, but fights occurred several times a day. Besides these boundary quarrels, the birds often deliberately trespassed on each other's territories. The rose hedge held a fascination for Uno and Una, and every now and then they foraged beneath it, sometimes returning home without the knowledge of the owner, but at other times being driven back in a hurry! 4M made his excursions alone, sometimes boldly on the wing, again stealthily on foot; but, whatever the method, the result was always dramatic.

While the presence of another Song Sparrow on the territory was not tolerated for an instant, other birds were also treated with conspicuous lack of hospitality. Eighteen species, ranging in size from the tiny Ruby-crowned Kinglet to the imposing Chewink, that weighs twice as much as a Song Sparrow, are recorded in my notes as being hustled off by Uno, and eleven of them by Una. Most of these were migrating sparrows and thrushes, over half of them larger than the birds that drove them. As to the birds nesting in the garden later in the season, the Song Sparrows seldom paid any attention to species larger than they—Robins, Cardinals, Catbirds, Brown Thrashers, and Mourning Doves, while smaller species —Maryland Yellowthroat, Indigo Buntings, and House Wrens —ducked into cover momentarily and proceeded with their several occupations. Two species, however, often failed to give way before the hostile approach of the owners of the territory; English Sparrows and Goldfinches as a rule took no notice of the threatened attack and continued to eat dandelion seeds or to sit placidly wherever they had alighted; with their bluff called, the only thing the Song Sparrows could do was to ignore these visitors.

One morning a curious thing happened: contrary to the feminine custom of keeping to low situations, Una flew to the top of a small tree and delivered a song. And *what* a song —a squeaky, unmusical affair of some six or seven notes, yet given with all the aplomb that Uno employed with his lovely melodies. On seven occasions during the last week of March I noted Una singing one or two of these foolish little ditties from a tree or the top of a weed, and the impression I gained was of something vestigial, something that had no meaning nowadays. Was this a relic of the earliest form of Melospizan song, existing before the sexes had differentiated their roles, the male developing it as an indispensable tool and a work of art into a thing of beauty, the female almost forgetting it?

For five days the south wind blew, and late March became balmier than May. This strange weather stirred the birds to a new activity:

"Mar. 21. To my astonishment Una has a long piece of dead grass. She flies east of the shed, Uno following her.

"Uno gets a double piece of grass. Flips wings. Goes into a tunnel in some rocks. Later gets an immense piece of grape-vine bark.

"Mar. 25. Uno's zeal in getting nesting material was the outstanding feature of today's session. He got several large loads, flying with them dangling from his bill. One he carried into a cavity in the rock pile, Una following him. He takes stuff to two places at opposite ends of his territory.

"Mar. 27. Uno and 4M are both occupied with nesting material, but their mates are mere spectators. Today I see coition for the first time, Una fluttering her wings beforehand, and saying *eee eee eee* directly after, but Uno makes no sound.

"Mar. 29. Una, as well as Uno, is now busy manipulating dead leaves, grass and bits of bark, but this interest has not crystallized into the definite project of nest building. Uno got six big loads and dropped them all. Una dropped most of hers."

March had seen stirring drama in our garden: the return of Uno from the South and the winning of his territory from the grasp of 4M; the tireless singing of both birds until the coming of their mates; the resolute defense of territories; and the symbolic nesting activities. Yet all this was but the first act in the age-old drama of the renewal of life upon the earth.

CHAPTER 2

Una Builds Three Nests

NESTING began in early April, hastened by the summerlike temperatures of late March. On the morning of the 6th I discovered that the Song Sparrow pair had entered a new phase in their activities: Una was building in earnest, while Uno watched. The location was different from any to which I had seen them carrying material during the last two weeks, yet it was only a few feet from the place where Uno's nest had been the previous May. In such cases it is often assumed that the same pair has built both nests; in this instance I knew that the male was the same, but the female different, since Uno's mate in 1928 had been unmistakably marked by the scar on her side. The present nest was on the ground, tucked well out of sight under a large burdock leaf.

Una's enthusiasm over this first nest was delightful to witness. With a large load in her bill, she flew chattering to the burdock above the site, dropped down out of sight for perhaps three-quarters of a minute, leaving again with another chatter. Her time schedule was arranged thus: fifteen, twenty, and twenty-three minutes at a stretch devoted to bringing loads every two or three minutes, interspersed with absences of five to eight minutes for lunch. Although this was probably the first time Una had ever built a nest, she proceeded surely and skilfully, and the finished product was the most substantial of any of the seven nests she made this year and the next.

Her labors, however, were sometimes interrupted:

"4M comes quietly into Uno's land, his tail twitching nervously. He comes into the south cherry, rapidly hops up the bank, and goes along it until he reaches the south end where Una is gathering nesting material. She discovers him and at once gives battle, starting him homeward. Uno comes dashing from the north end and finishes sending him home, being in turn driven back by 4M and his mate."

The next day Una was working as busily as ever. Here is a ten-minute record in the morning:

"6:13. Una chatters as she flies from the nest; comes near Uno, says *eee eee eee* with fluttering wings. He approaches, she says *zhee* and turns away, tugging and tugging at dead grass, getting a great load.

"6:16. She flies silently, stays forty-seven seconds at the nest. Leaves silently; gives a *chunk* as she alights, preens, then gets more material and flies with a large load. I don't know where Uno is.

"6:17. Fight on 4M's land; apparently Uno was trespassing, and 4M sends him home in a hurry, both birds singing. Una comes dashing to the scene, shouting *eee eee eee*. Then gets another mouthful, flies below nest, *chunk,* then continues her journey.

"6:22. Another load; she stays twenty-nine seconds; flies out silently; gets more material with much expenditure of energy."

On the 8th Una was building slowly, taking tiny pieces one

at a time and staying several minutes on each trip to the nest. Quarta, in the meantime, was carrying large loads to a location west of the rose hedge. While she was busied in this occupation, a female Cowbird alighted on a near-by post; Quarta instantly froze, letting her piece of grass fall. 4M appeared at once and began to object—*chunk, chunk, chunk.* The Cowbird dropped to the ground as if to search for the nest, whereupon the Song Sparrows fell upon her, bill and claw, and she retreated before their onslaught.

Now the Song Sparrows started to sing once more. With their mates occupied in preparing homes for eggs and babies, Uno and 4M and the others again filled the countryside with their glad and varied songs.

On the 10th Una's nest held its first egg, grey-blue with splotches of crushed strawberry color. The next day there was another, but on the third morning, alas, instead of three eggs there was but one. After examining this disappointing state of affairs, I took up my usual post some thirty feet to the west. Soon a female Cowbird came chattering to the burdock over the nest. Uno and Una hurried up and objected *chunk, chunk;* she dropped down to the nest, stayed there about fifteen seconds, and reappeared; the Song Sparrows rushed to attack her with loud *zhee, zhees.* Off she flew with another chatter. Una went to the nest and left immediately. I looked, but found nothing changed. Even though the pair had given up the nest, the tie had not been entirely broken and defense reactions had been called into play by the visit of the Cowbird. I never knew what had broken up the nest.

Twenty minutes after this adventure Uno and Una began to hunt nesting sites, flipping their wings, making soft little noises, and carrying dead grass hither and yon. The weather had turned cold, and it was not until the 17th that Una began to build again, very secretively, some ten yards to the

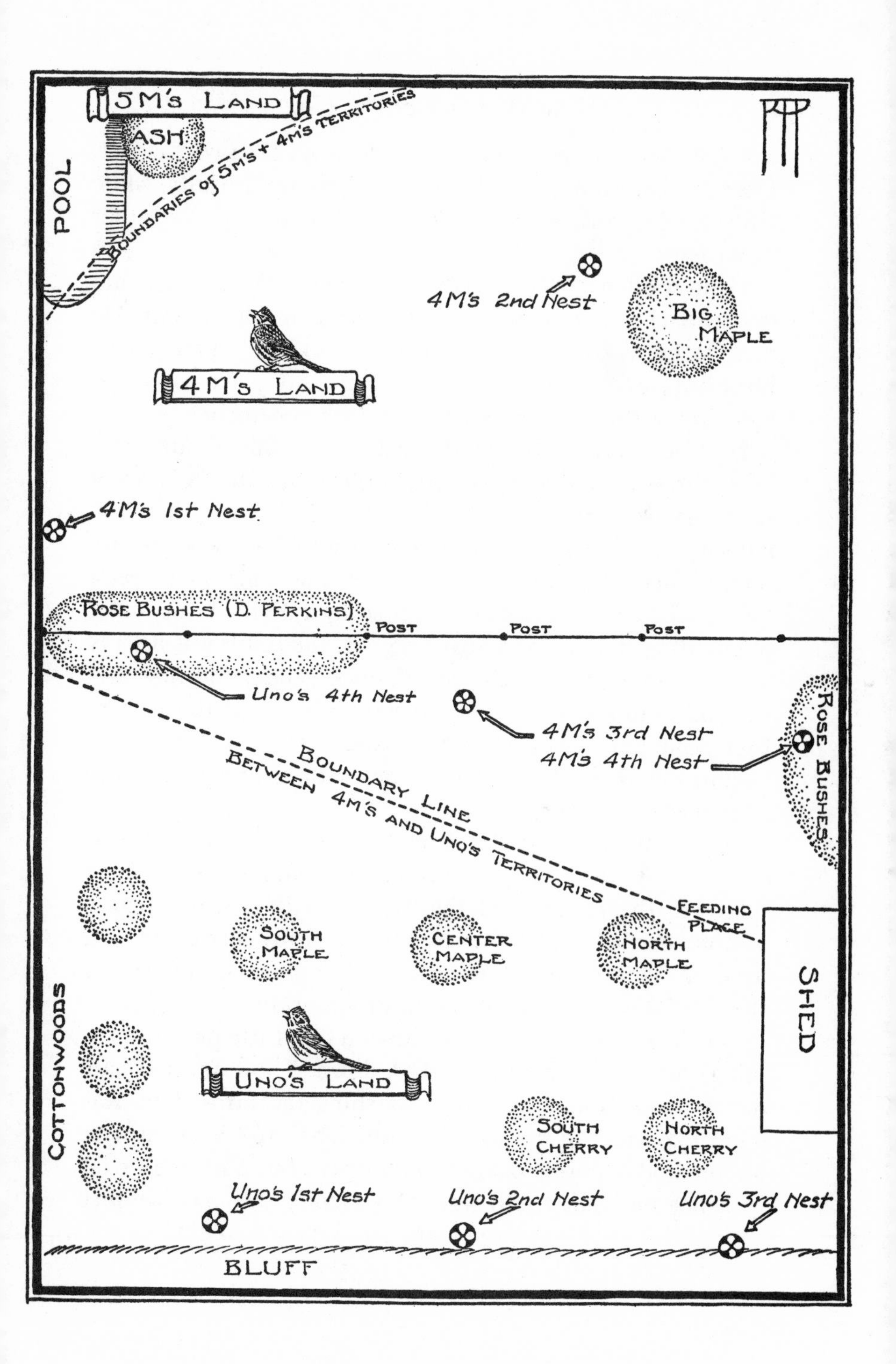
5M's Land
Ash
Pool
Boundaries of 5M's + 4M's Territories
4M's 2nd Nest
Big Maple
4M's Land
4M's 1st Nest
Rose Bushes (D. Perkins)
Post
Post
Post
Uno's 4th Nest
4M's 3rd Nest
4M's 4th Nest
Rose Bushes
Boundary Line
Between 4M's and Uno's Territories
Feeding Place
South Maple
Center Maple
North Maple
Shed
Cottonwoods
Uno's Land
South Cherry
North Cherry
Uno's 1st Nest
Uno's 2nd Nest
Uno's 3rd Nest
Bluff

east, making a flimsy nest, well hidden under sweet clover. Here she laid four eggs and incubated them faithfully, while Uno stood guard, amusing himself with singing and other activities:

"Uno suddenly flies directly west over the rose hedge and swings back home with 4M and Quarta in hot pursuit. He sings as he lands in safety, puffed out and tail spread. Una joins him, exclaiming *zhee, zhee*. Uno and 4M have a real fight, while their mates expostulate with vehement *zhees*."

Uno very rarely visited the nest itself, but about every twenty to thirty minutes he came within three to six yards of it and gave a song loud and clear, what I came to call a "signal song." Sometimes Una merely answered *eee eee eee* and stayed where she was, but more often she came off to get a bite to eat. Uno was then confronted by a divided duty—that of guarding the nest and guarding her; the result was usually a compromise, a few minutes of singing near the nest and then off to join her. After six to eight minutes in the garden, back came Una, escorted by her mate.

This sounds peaceful enough, but with 4M next door, life never became monotonous:

"Una comes flying out from the nest, scolding *chunk, chunk*. 4M attacks her, knocking her off her perch. Uno speeds to the rescue, and the two males have a rough-and-tumble battle, while Quarta hurries near chattering and scolding. Uno returns singing, and Una greets him with *eee eee eee*. Then she goes to the feeding station."

The babies hatched on May 5th and 6th, little pinkish bare things adorned with tufts of black down. I now devoted four hours a day instead of two to watching the birds; Uno was a great comfort to me with his confidence and his conspicuous method of going to and from the nest, but Una was a trial with her nervous, timid ways. Apparently this was her first experience with family responsibilities, for she continued to treat her charges as though they were eggs. Fortunately Uno rose to the occasion and brought the necessary nourishment, while Una was satisfied with keeping the babies warm.

It was a busy life they led, as this half-hour's record of May 9th shows:

"8:11. Uno fed, then went to the seeds [i.e., the feeding station]. Una off, then back again.

"8:13. Fed again, stayed at the nest 14.5 seconds by the stop watch. Una off to chase a Whitethroat. Uno gave a song; Una went to the seeds.

"8:17. He feeds, stays 17 seconds. She returns without food. He drives a Whitethroat, then a Lincoln's Sparrow.

"8:23. He feeds, stays 18.5 seconds; she goes off and on again.

"8:28. He feeds, stays 29 seconds. She goes to seeds; he sings.

"8:32. 4M is on the fallen tree, staring down at Una who is having a difference with Quarta.

"8:35. Uno feeds, stays 28 seconds. To seeds; a fight with 4M. Una back to nest; actually has a caterpillar!

"8:37. Una dashes out, driving the pair of House Wrens away from the vicinity of her nest.

"8:41. Uno feeds, stays 24 seconds."

On this day Una began really to help feed the young, bringing a third as many meals as did Uno, and the next day half as many. During the ten days that the young were in the nest, I spent thirty-nine hours watching it, seeing Uno bring food 367 times and Una 113 times, an average of twelve meals per hour for the whole period. The rate of feeding increases as the young grow, a brood of tiny young being fed perhaps five times an hour, middle-sized young about fifteen times, while during the last three days of nest life the rate may reach twenty-five or more meals an hour. Parental activity varies with the number of young in the nest, for the more children there are, the harder do father and mother work.

The baby Song Sparrows changed rapidly in looks; when nine days old they were as pretty as could be, and welcomed the arrival of meals with a veritable clamor. The night of May 14th rain came down in torrents; the next morning two young lay dead in the nest, but the other two, happily, were out in the wide world. Uno and Una were using new alarm notes—shrill *icks* and loud *ticks,* as I tried to locate their precious babes—an almost impossible task, so closely did the little things hide in the weeds. Pleading *zee zee zees* arose from two spots, and the parents made many trips each hour, Uno caring for one child, and Una the other.

For the first week of life in the open Song Sparrow etiquette is summed up in the motto: Children should be heard and not seen. Seven days after leaving the nest the young things come out into society—fluffy, buffy, bobtailed darlings able to use their wings for the first time. Una's baby was a wild little creature, much more timid than either parent. Uno's baby began to tease as soon as father came near, meeting him with fluttering wings and enthusiastic cries, following him and begging for more. Day by day their voices grew louder, as they flew to meet their parents or pursued them.

Both youngsters became more and more devoted to their father, for Una took up a new interest; on May 21st she started to build in the "nest-tangle," the place which she had particularly liked in late March. Here she worked industriously and quietly, getting materials close at hand, while Uno at intervals watched her labors from a near-by burdock. On the 24th she laid the first of four eggs, three of which hatched after twelve days' incubation. I had expected more efficient behavior from her this time; but no, these babies, like the last, were treated like eggs for the first half of nest life. On June 17th and 18th a little over a month after the fledging of the May brood, these three babies left the nest. One of them returned the next spring to nest within sight of her birthplace; and the following year one of her sons took up his territory next to the home of his grandparents.

What, in the meantime, had 4M and Quarta been doing besides pestering their neighbors? Their first nest, built just west of the rose hedge, had been broken up while it contained eggs; and the same misfortune had attended their second nest, situated under the big maple. The third nest was placed east of the rose hedge, and here at last success crowned their efforts, for under the watchful care of the two parents four babies had been fledged on June 15th.

Both pairs had made three attempts to nest. Uno and Una had succeeded in bringing five offspring safely off the nest, and 4M and Quarta four. Raising children is a strenuous occupation; father has scant time to sing, and both parents grow thin in satisfying the boundless appetites of their clamorous offspring. Yet there is no need to pity the "poor overworked parents." As Oskar Heinroth writes, "A bird has no parental duties, only parental pleasures, and only does what, so to speak, is 'fun' for him."

CHAPTER 3

The Nest in the Rose Hedge

NOW that Uno and Una had three nests to their credit and two families safely fledged, I expected them to rest on their laurels. But not a bit of it. On June 20th, two days after the last baby had left the nest, Una was tugging once more at twigs.

Even more astonishing than her undiminished zeal was the place where she was getting material. It was none other than the rose hedge—*4M's rose hedge!* This patch of briars had held a fascination for Uno and Una from the beginning, and many a time 4M had sent them scurrying home from beneath its dark recesses. Within the last few days one of Una's children had settled there, and Una, as she brought it food, evidently found within the blossoming tangle the very place that suited her fancy for her next nest. Of course she had no business to fix upon a spot in her neighbor's territory; she had transgressed the laws of territory, and trouble was sure to follow.

I put my camp stool under the south maple, arranged the feeding station with its bread and bird seed under the center maple, and prepared to watch developments. The birds cooperated by accepting me as part of the environment.

Quarta, who was building in the rosebush to the north, came over, all hunched up, to threaten Una, following her till she flew home. Back she came in a few minutes to build once more. 4M dashed for her; she crouched, said *zhee,* and left.

The next day, when 4M was not watching, Uno and Una made an expedition together into the rose hedge, giving the pretty nest call. I believe that Una was not consulting her husband in regard to her audacious scheme, but was merely showing him where the nest was to be. Soon 4M's vigilance was aroused; he savagely drove Uno away whenever the latter came anywhere near the rose hedge. In spite of this, Una grew more and more determined. On June 23rd she was scolding on the post above her nest; 4M flew at her; she gave a resolute *zhee* and stood her ground. He flew at her again; she countered with louder *zhees,* and *he* retreated. She flew over to a bush on 4M's side of the hedge and preened herself. Her nest was there, hence that was *her* land, and she paid no attention to 4M's wrath.

Uno alighted on a dead tree lying some ten feet east of the rose hedge and within his own territory; 4M followed him. Uno at first retreated, then plucked up courage to face him; and the result was a fight. 4M flew to a post in the hedge and started to sing, but stopped short in the middle of a song at the sight of Una gathering lining for her nest right below him. However, as she continued to work, he resumed his singing.

Since the first three nests of Una and Quarta had been placed on the ground, I searched and searched through the prickly rose hedge and the north rosebush for nests in low situations, only to discover at last that each bird had built her fourth nest three feet above the ground. On June 24th

Una laid her first egg, while Quarta's nest already held its full complement of three.

With mother thus occupied, the babies showered their attentions on father. Father Song Sparrow is a long-suffering individual; he doesn't take offense when his children stand on his toes, or land on his back, or knock him from his perch:

"Baby pursuing 4M. Baby calling constantly. 4M twitters fiercely in alarm; baby stops his cries instantly. 4M twitters and twitters, shooing it under the bushes away from me.

"Nearly every song that 4M gives is a signal for a child to pop up beside him."

Life for the Song Sparrow husband and father in the midst of the nesting season is a complicated affair at best; he has an incubating wife to protect, troublesome neighbors to watch, a brood of young hopefuls to feed, and his own living to get, not to mention keeping himself and his family out of the clutches of prowling enemies. The reason that he can successfully cope with such a multiplicity of details is that he does one thing at a time with all his might, and in the next minute, perhaps, turns his whole attention to something else.

It is evident that the normal program would keep any bird busy enough, but Una had enormously complicated matters by violating the code of territory and thus upsetting the accepted rules of conduct. She had been able to achieve her end by stout resistance to 4M, unaided by her husband, who had always been dominated by his powerful neighbor. On June 25th, however, there was a brief reversal of this status. 4M had entered the trap, and I pulled the string; Uno flew to the top of the cage and started to fight the prisoner. Before I reached them, a side door fell in and 4M escaped. Uno was so elated over his momentary triumph over his ancient enemy that he attacked Quarta for the first time to my knowledge; she resisted, and for a minute or two there was quite a fierce little battle.

The next turn of events was unexpected: 4M suffered a temporary lapse of interest in his territory, his wife, and her nest, and took a vacation with the children in the far end of his land. Was the anomalous situation in which his rose hedge was occupied by his neighbor's wife so baffling to him that he simply ran away from his difficulties? Whatever the explanation, his watchful care was relaxed—a state of affairs which made a great difference in our garden.

Uno was in the highest of spirits, calling Una off the nest, feeding his children, and, in particular, lording it over Quarta. There was no other bird that came swinging around to the feeding station with the perfect confidence he showed, the others approaching by degrees, hesitating, doubtful. He even perched upon the posts along the rose hedge—4M's very special property.

Quarta, on the other hand, was far from enjoying herself. She missed 4M not only for his company, but also in his role of policeman. On June 26th, as she started towards the trap for an early breakfast, there on the top was Uno crouched and menacing. She changed her course only to have him circle above her with a song, to which she responded *zhee*. Because of 4M's neglect she had to drive intruders from her home bush—House Wrens, English Sparrows, and young Robins. She even said *zhee* to a baby cottontail, but without making any visible impression.

She had been accustomed to coming off the nest at rather short intervals—only sixteen and seventeen minutes, but on the 26th her husband failed to come to sing her off the nest and she stayed on waiting in vain for him, once for thirty-three minutes and once for forty. When at last he did appear,

Quarta Scolds a Baby Cottontail

she rushed out to greet him. And loneliness was not all she suffered from, for Uno seized the opportunity to "pounce" upon her. Pouncing is a preliminary overture in Song Sparrow courtship, the means apparently by which the male shows that he is master. The technique is as follows: the male suddenly darts down at the female, collides with her, and flies away with a loud song. He pounces on his own wife at the beginning of each nesting cycle, and also at times on his neighbors' wives if they chance to be unprotected, treating them much more roughly than he does his own mate. 4M had pounced on Una many times, but never until now had I seen Uno pouncing on Quarta.

On the 27th things were going from bad to worse. The day before, 4M had appeared every twenty to twenty-seven minutes during the morning to get meals at the lunch counter; but today he came just three times in as many hours, once absenting himself for an hour and a quarter at a stretch. I noted:

"7:31. Quarta flies to her rosebush. That miserable Uno attacks her; she fights back, *zhee-zheeing* fiercely; he flies away singing.

"8:23. 4M actually sings; Quarta answers with a loud *eee eee eee*. I'm thankful to see that he hasn't forgotten his wife entirely. At this stage during the last nesting he was as devoted as could be.

"8:40. Again Uno pounces on Quarta; sings as he stands there; sings as he flies away. If 4M were only on the job!"

So the invaders triumphed, but not for long. Retribution was close at hand. On the morning of June 28th something happened which I would have given a great deal to see. Unfortunately on that day a combination of rain and household duties kept me indoors, and it was not until late afternoon that I was able to visit them. At once the question arose in my mind: Where is Uno?

"What *has* become of him? . . . His babies are hungry and calling. . . . They feel deserted, and so do I."

Seven faint songs from the southwest were the only evidence of Uno's existence in the two hours that I watched. 4M was back once more, feeding young and calling Quarta off the nest.

Meal-time

The next morning I was out early to try to solve the mystery. I heard a Song Sparrow *chunk* on the southeast bank and then give soft *tsips:*

"It is Uno! What *has* happened to him to change him into such a different bird—retiring, silent, oblivious of the seeds? His feathers look a bit ruffled.

"A baby discovers him and pursues him closely. Uno gives it a small tidbit, while baby flutters. Uno appears worn out.

"Uno's baby hops on his back in its eagerness, slipping off again. Uno catches an insect for it."

Uno was a very subdued, modest, quiet bird that morning. By afternoon he seemed to be recovering some of his normal spirits. 4M appeared a number of times, but showed no disposition to guard his territory.

The next day Uno was his old self again except that he stood in great awe of 4M. Gradually I realized what must have happened: 4M must have caught Uno abusing Quarta and given him a punishment that he long remembered.

Not only did Uno fear 4M; he even hurried away at the approach of Quarta! It was a strange situation indeed, with Uno not venturing to sing near his own nest, and afraid to drive 4M away when *he* sang right above it. In this predicament Una again had the sole burden of defending her position, and she uttered *zhee* loudly and emphatically with widespread tail whenever she met 4M, with the consequence that he avoided her. Territory lines had broken down, and the whole pattern of behavior rested merely on personal relationships, 4M and Quarta dominating Uno, but being dominated by Una. Uno's young were due to hatch in a few days. How were the birds to extricate themselves from this impasse?

CHAPTER 4

Uno Wins the Rose Hedge

THE value of territory to the Song Sparrow could hardly have been more clearly demonstrated than by the occurrences in our garden in late June and July, 1929. Una had broken with custom; territorial lines had been temporarily forgotten with unfortunate results, but 4M's renewed insistence on denying Uno access to his nest was bound to spell disaster to a brood of young. The only way out was recourse to the territory establishment procedure.

On July 1st I saw the first manifestation, a boundary dispute near Una's nest; Uno had just got a billful of bread when 4M came to threaten him; they hopped about, Uno singing with the bread in his mouth. The next day I witnessed three of these ceremonial territory establishments, east of the rose hedge between 6:45 and 8:45 in the morning, 4M playing the part of the silent, menacing overlord, Uno that of the singing challenger. 4M's pose meant, "You have no right on my land." Uno's singing meant: "This is really my land. I intend to settle here." Then each retired well within his boundaries and hurled defiance at the other, with the consequence that singing, ordinarily at a low ebb at this time of year, rose to a high pitch with both birds.

It was an exciting life for me with so much happening in the garden: Uno and 4M trying to settle their controversy according to the code of territory, Una upsetting all precedent by humbling the redoubtable 4M, and the engaging interplay between Uno and his children:

"July 3. Una to the seeds, says *zhee zhee* at sight of 4M puffed up near by. Goes for him, and he retreats.

"Uno feeds a demonstrative child; goes to feeding station, child flies north. He returns with bread to the dead tree where he left babe; seems surprised to see no one, says *tsip, tsip* and goes into box elder.

"July 4. Baby comes to seeds, saying *see? see?* Eats away busily, until Uno alights; at once it becomes a baby and is fed again and again.

"4M drives off one of Uno's children; goes for it three times.

"One of Uno's children pecks at another. Uno flies to the seeds, followed by a baby. He pecks at it!

"July 5. Baby has been feeding busily; Uno comes; baby starts to beg; Uno pecks at it, but the next moment relents and feeds it, baby bowing in a ridiculous manner.

"Baby eats seeds rapidly by itself, constantly squealing and fluttering one wing!"

4M had been pursued by his loving offspring until the 3rd of July, at which time he perhaps made it plain to them that at the age of four weeks it is time for little Song Sparrows to make their own way in the world. On the 5th of July at nine A.M. I examined Quarta's nest and found an infant lying between the broken halves of the shell. Quarta did not leave again until 9:45, when she came off chattering. Since 4M did not seem to be in the vicinity, she probably did not meet him during her eight-minute outing. At 10:22 she left again, and 4M, who had been singing near by for nine minutes, darted after her. Three minutes later he appeared, sang twice on the post near the nest, and then *went in to look at the nest.* At 10:29 he returned with a small insect, and baby received its first meal. This raised a new question: how did Quarta tell 4M that something had happened?

Conflict between 4M and Uno

The crisis in the territorial conflict came on July 6th. Again and again 4M came over by the rose hedge, tormenting Uno, who again and again put in his claim for the land by his rapid singing, while both hopped about near each other. At nine o'clock 4M drove one of Uno's children; Uno hurried to the scene, and there was a fight. Then began another ceremony. This time Una lent a hand, saying *zhee zhee* as she viciously went for 4M, who quickly retreated. Back and forth went the two males, back and forth within a few inches of each other. At last the crisis came; the two birds grappled, fighting desperately on the ground, attacking each other again and again. Finally 4M flew off and sang; Uno did the same.

And half an hour later he had the satisfaction of singing right over his own nest.

So the victory was won, and Uno was in possession of the hedge at last. And only just in time, for on July 7th at 7:24 A.M. I found the first baby had hatched.

Now I hoped to discover how mother Song Sparrow informs father of the great event. Una went to the seeds, but Uno came to the hedge to object to my interest, so the pair did not meet. Fifteen minutes later, what should I see but a sizable garter snake at the base of Una's rosebush! Uno was hopping and hopping about it silently; suddenly he gave it a peck, whereupon it darted its head at him. Another peck and the snake uncoiled and crawled into the hedge. This caused so much excitement among the Nice family that Una's and Uno's encounter at the seeds passed unnoticed. The pair returned, *twitching their wings;* both went to the nest; Uno left and returned in eight minutes with the first meal.

The snake did not reappear to disturb the precious nest, but his visit could hardly have been more inopportune. I never had the chance in later years to witness the meeting of mother and father after the hatching of the first egg. I can only piece together the evidence from these two experiences. I believe that mother betrays excitement by flipping her wings, upon which father visits the nest; doubtless baby lifts its wobbly head and opens its rose-lined mouth, and father knows exactly what to do next.

Another curious thing happened on July 7th: 4M pounced on Una. As long as Una had the sole responsibility of protecting her nest and herself from 4M, she had to make herself formidable by exaggerated hostility. Now, however, that that bit of land was ceded to Uno, Una once more slipped back into the role of mere neighbor's wife, and as such a legitimate object for pouncing—in case neighbor was not there.

Ill luck again followed 4M and Quarta; something, possibly a rat, possibly a snake, took two of their small babies, so only one remained. This left 4M with plenty of leisure for stirring up his neighbors; but Uno, as owner of the rose hedge, could afford to indulge in boundary disputes without detriment to the welfare of his babies. His grown children were loath to give him up; on the 8th they still called for food, on the 10th and 11th they twitched wings hopefully on meeting him, but he merely hurried away. On the 12th I noted, "Both fathers drive off their own children."

The new babies were the pride of Uno's heart. He brought them tiny insects and stood over them lovingly for many minutes at a time, Una often having difficulty in dislodging him. He even sang while perched on the rim of the nest! Una, for her part, had at last discovered that little babies are different from eggs and brought them food almost from the start.

So the Song Sparrows' strenuous labors drew to a close. Early on the morning of July 17th we had to bid good-by to our friends in the garden, since we were leaving for the East. Quarta's and 4M's nest stood empty as their baby had left the day before. Peace reigned about the nest in the rose hedge where four pretty youngsters were nearly fledged.

CHAPTER 5

Uno and Una Return

A BIRD decorated with colored bands possesses an individuality far above that of his fellows, for they definitely identify the bird bearing them to the observer, and the confusion and uncertainty that until lately have accompanied so much field work vanish. My study of Song Sparrows would have been impossible without the traps and the red, yellow, green, blue, and black celluloid bands.

With the Song Sparrow there is another characteristic that sets each male apart from the others, and that is his manner of singing. In contrast to almost all other North American birds, each Song Sparrow sings songs that are different from those of every other Song Sparrow. During the long hours of association with the birds in the spring and summer of 1929, I had learned each of Uno's and 4M's songs by heart, so that I knew each one of them as well as I did the songs, for instance, of a Maryland Yellowthroat or a Warbling Vireo. I had known the year before that 4M possessed a variety of distinctive songs, and I had recorded four of them; but in regard to Uno I had noted, "He appears to have only two songs, neither especially distinctive." It was not an easy matter for me to distinguish and recognize each separate song. I began with the more striking ones, memorized their characteristic portions, and recorded them as they sounded to me both in syllables and in dots, dashes, and curlicues, gradually building up the rest of the songs around the main themes. Each song was given a letter and, once thoroughly mastered, was thus recorded in my notebooks whenever heard.

This course of intensive ear training showed me that Uno possessed six songs, and 4M nine. Others of my Song Sparrows have had larger repertoires—twelve, fifteen, and perhaps more songs; but with only one other bird (187M in 1934) did I learn by heart every single song. Some songs were recorded for most of the males with whom I came in contact, and many of these songs I recognized instantly; but only by concentration on a few birds can their whole repertoire be learned.

The definite knowledge of Uno's and 4M's songs whenever heard was an important aid to me when listening to the birds from the sleeping porch in the early morning hours, and from my study during the day. It also proved an added source of happiness, for I became aware of character and loveliness to which I had formerly been oblivious. 4M's song *A* had a determined, almost grim sound; with *C,* he seemed in a desperate hurry; *G* was light and airy—a charming song; and *K* was the prettiest of all, with the gayest little lilt at the end. Uno's *H* was spirited, and his *C* had a triumphant ring, while *F* was high and clear, of exquisite, haunting beauty. Indeed, as far as variety of singing went, it was as if fifteen birds of different species had settled on our grounds.

When we returned to Columbus in the fall of 1929 we found Uno and 4M and 5M in our garden; quarreling was at a minimum as territories were no longer defended. Uno left for the South on the night of October 14th, and 5M was not seen after the 18th; but 4M lingered on through October and even through November. On December 2nd cold weather had set in, accompanied by a four-inch snow; when I found him, his feathers all puffed out against the cold, eating weed seeds in company with Tree Sparrows, Juncos, and Cardinals, it seemed certain to me that he would stay through the winter. To find that some of our nesting Song Sparrows migrated South for the winter, and that some remained, was an unexpected and exciting discovery. It was a particular pleasure to look forward to having 4M's company all year long.

The second half of January was bleak and snowy; but with February came mild and sunny days that started all the resident Song Sparrows to singing. 4M made expeditions across the road to bother 7M, a young male just taking up his territory; 7M puffed out his feathers, waved his wings like little flags, and sang his best to defend his land from 4M. On the 13th, 4M settled down to proclaim his own territory, singing on his own land—and Uno's too. He gave 178 songs in one hour and 211 in the next, giving each song for many minutes at a time before beginning another.

On the 22nd his singing had almost ceased, and I went out to investigate, armed, as always, with the bird glasses:

"A wonderful Song Sparrow chorus on every side. But 4M is sitting silent in his big maple. An unbanded Song Sparrow comes to the tree; he flies to a post, the new bird follows. He sits silent and looks down at her. She eats, then comes to join him. He flies to the rose hedge; she follows. He approaches; she says *zhee;* he leaves. She says *tsip*. He returns."

So a mate had arrived! And so very early! She was not Quarta since she had no band. She was a dark bird, tame and voluble. I named her Quatre.

The next morning something happened that I recorded in gigantic letters in my field book:

"UNO IS BACK!"

There is always a happy thrill for the bird bander when one of his birds returns, after a journey to the South or the North. This thrill was heightened a hundredfold for me, since Uno was such a special bird; I had followed his fortunes for two years, and during the last year had come to know him so well and to love him so dearly that I was jubilant to have him home once more. I rejoiced in every one of his familiar songs; never had they sounded sweeter.

4M, of course, was welcoming him in proper Melospizan style:

"8:25. Uno singing *F* constantly. 4M singing *J* steadily. 4M chasing Uno around and about. Quatre adding her sixpence; she joins the chase with a chatter. . . .

"8:45. A fourth bird appears. 4M and Quatre dash off in pursuit. Uno sits in triumph in his cottonwood, singing *C*. Preens himself, then sings *A*. . . .

"8:50. Uno puffed, lifts one wing, sings *G*. 4M silent, but soon both sing. 4M chasing Uno, Quatre usually tagging after. Most of the flights revolve around the rose hedge. . . .

"9:26. Birds return from a prolonged chase. Uno sings *F*, *F*. Fight, chase. . . .

"9:41. Uno puffed, wing fluttering, is pursued by 4M and wife. Soon 4M stops and gets a big twig; he and Quatre are on the ground together. Uno comes down; 4M drops his twig. . . .

"10:00. Uno to the feeding station, gets two bites. 4M comes; Uno leaves, sings *K*, *K*. 4M gets two bites. . . .

"10:06. 4M and Quatre on ground feeding. She gets a twig and drops it."

This, to my surprise, was the end of their quarrels, Uno conquering his territory *including the rose hedge* without even a regular territory establishment procedure. I witnessed but a single small fight; but perhaps I missed a bigger one when the birds were out of my sight for two minutes. Whenever 4M gave Uno a little respite, back the latter would fly over the rose hedge. After all the grief of the previous season, he was going to settle that bone of contention from the start.

The energy displayed by Uno that morning was amazing. After the journey of the night before, for two hours there

Soon 4M Gets a Big Twig

had been continual fleeing from 4M and constant singing (270 songs in one hour), with only four momentary stops to snatch a bite of food. It did not seem in character for 4M to give up the contest so quickly. Was it that Uno was older and more confident, and 4M older and less overflowing with excess energy, or did the presence of Quatre have anything to do with it? Possibly he now preferred a life of quiet domesticity to incessant bickerings. He dominated Uno this year as last, but the situation along the border was more a state of armed neutrality than the open warfare of the previous season.

In the meanwhile I had been looking every day for 5M, the bird that owned the ash tree and pool just west of 4M's territory. Although he had been on the ground early in 1929 (I had banded him February 9th) and had what I considered the best territory thereabouts because of the water on it, and although he sang faithfully, he was the last of the four males in the immediate neighborhood to get a mate, as Quarta had joined 4M March 13th, and Una joined Uno March 15th, while 6M, nesting across the road south of our house, had got his mate the earliest of all, March 11th. It was not until March 21 that 5M could take a vacation from constant singing; his mate was an amusingly talkative, demonstrative little body. Unfortunately in late April after she had built her nest, something went wrong; one day I was shocked to see that she had lost her tail, and the next day she vanished. 5M mounted his ash and sang incessantly; for six weeks he sang before patience was rewarded by the coming of a second mate. Three babies were hatched in a nest at the base of the ash; all left the nest safely with bands upon their legs.

This year I was delighted to find on February 25th that 5M had come, but–his territory was firmly in the possession of 8M, a young resident:

"7:30. 8M chases 5M around and about continually, sometimes going for him viciously. Both sing. 5M chippers. He constantly returns to his former land, but 8M keeps the upper hand. . . .

"8:07. A fight near the ash. 5M singing on the ground, following 8M, who only feeds. Neither is puffed. 5M goes into the ash, sings, then faces 8M and they hit each other. 5M chases another Song Sparrow from the ash, then returns to 8M. His tail is spread. 8M now singing. 5M drives him, then back to the ash and sings and sings.

"8:12. 5M singing, 8M threatening. 8M advancing, 5M retreating.

"8:24. Both in ash, both singing and threatening each other. 8M flies to the east, but retires when Uno meets him all puffed out.

"8:37. Now 5M pursuing 8M; both sing. *Now 5M is the despot,* following 8M, bumping into him.

"8:42. 5M pursuing constantly. Now a flying chase—a fierce battle, rolling over and over.

"8:57. 5M chasing 8M; they skirt the corner of 4M's land; 4M rushes in and joins the pursuit."

5M had recovered his ash, but he was not easily rid of 8M. Whenever I visited them throughout the day, there was endless chasing. 8M had yielded to 5M's claim, but was trying to squeeze in a territory between Uno on the east, 4M on the north, and 5M on the west.

As the days passed, 8M was tolerated by his neighbors as long as he stayed in an absurdly small area; whenever he tried to enlarge his boundaries on either side, he was met with determined resistance from 5M or Uno. These two sang morning, noon, and afternoon, while little was heard from 4M, who led a contented life with his devoted Quatre. On February 27th, however, 4M was singing once more; something had killed his mate.

Two days later a new mate had arrived, also unbanded; she was a silent bird, light in color. In order to find an appropriate name for the newcomer I looked in the dictionary under the word "four," choosing what struck me as the most engaging synonym—namely Chatvar, from the Sanskrit.

On March 10th Uno stopped singing:

"I believe a lady has arrived. She is unbanded. She comes near Uno; he walks about with crest raised, then flies to the rose hedge with tail spread. She flies there with a pretty little chatter. He is above her; she says *zhee,* then *eee eee eee.*"

The dictionary was again consulted, this time under "one"; I chose the Dutch word *een* for Uno's wife. With both 4M and Uno already mated, what, I wondered, would Quarta and Una do, should they return?

The Ides of March proved full of import to 5M, for both happiness and trouble arrived on that day for him in the shape of a mate and a new neighbor, the irrepressible 10M. This bird had fixed his affections upon 8M's bit of land (8M having disappeared overnight) and now embarked upon the ambitious project of acquiring and enlarging this territory for himself. The neighborhood was in an uproar. 5M, Uno, and 4M each took a hand in trying to make him see that there was no land to let in that region; but the more he was rebuffed, the more stubbornly he stuck to his enterprise. Uno had been singing some two songs an hour as befitted a newly married man, but he was so outraged by 10M's impudence that from 8:20 to 9:20 that morning he sang no fewer than 278 times!

As regards 5M's mate, I was excited to see that *she had a band upon her left leg.* Could she be Una without her colored band, or was she one of the young birds? (After this I made it an invariable rule to put the aluminum band on the right leg with all nestlings, and on the left leg with all older birds.) How should I capture her? Up to that time it had not occurred to me to take my trap afield with me, and I had used it only near the house and in the garden. But it was plain I should have to catch her on her own territory. So I took the only trap I owned at that time, a small pull-string affair, and baited it under the ash, while with the end of the cord held hopefully in my hand, a Patience on a gravel heap, I waited on the opposite bank. The lady, however, proved

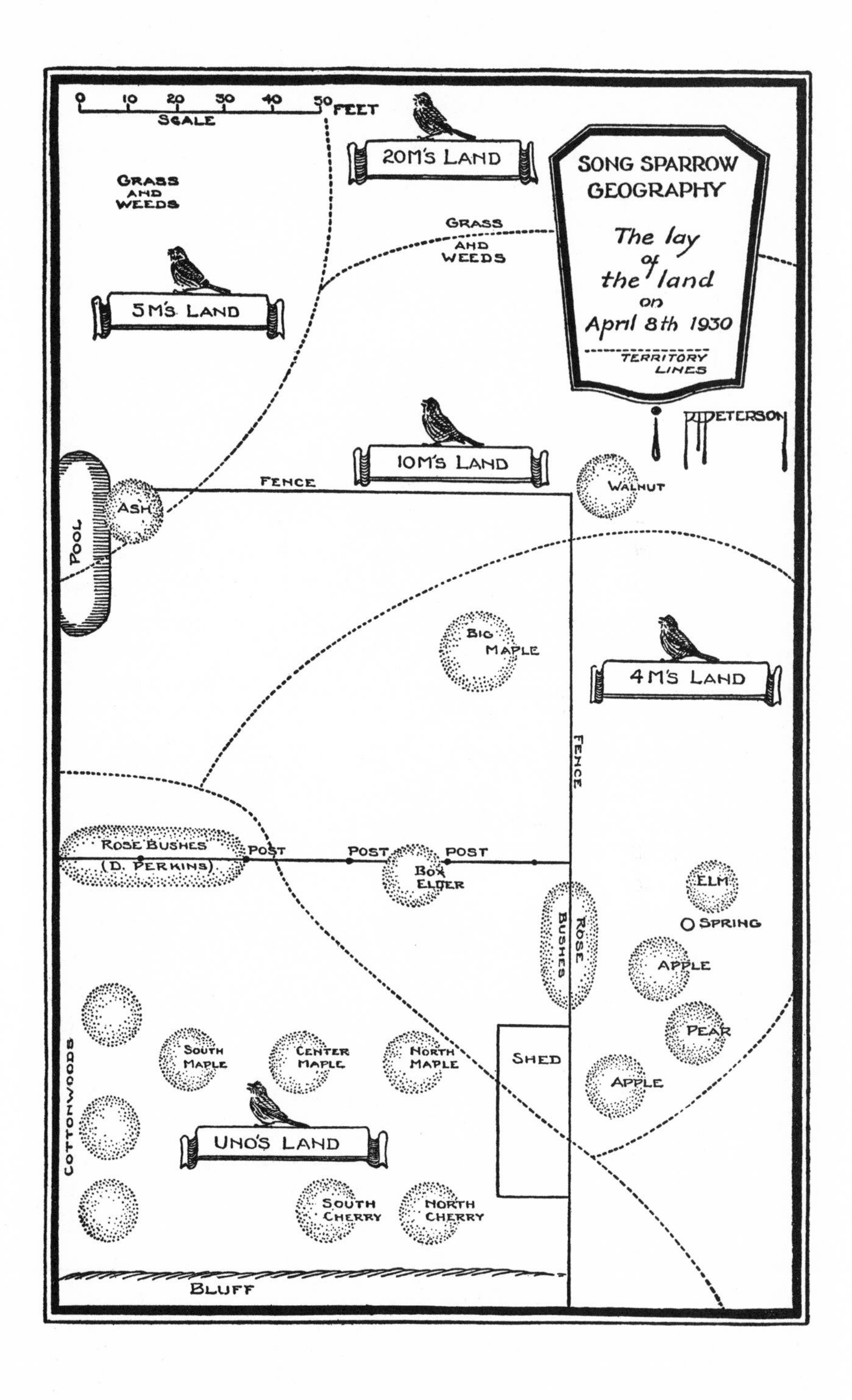
0 10 20 30 40 50 FEET
SCALE
SONG SPARROW GEOGRAPHY
The lay of the land on April 8th 1930
TERRITORY LINES
GRASS AND WEEDS
20M'S LAND
GRASS AND WEEDS
5M'S LAND
10M'S LAND
FENCE
POOL
ASH
WALNUT
BIG MAPLE
4M'S LAND
FENCE
ROSE BUSHES (D. PERKINS)
POST
POST
POST
BOX ELDER
ELM
SPRING
ROSE BUSHES
APPLE
PEAR
SHED
APPLE
SOUTH MAPLE
CENTER MAPLE
NORTH MAPLE
COTTONWOODS
UNO'S LAND
SOUTH CHERRY
NORTH CHERRY
BLUFF
R. T. PETERSON

cautious, and six chilly hours on four different mornings passed with the capture of no one but 10M. But if tangible results of these mornings were few, many pages of notebook were filled with the doings of the birds and in particular a complete count of all the songs given by the four males in whom I was most interested. The three mated birds sang as follows: Uno gave from zero to 26 songs an hour, 4M gave from 3 to 20, and 5M from 3 to 21, but the bachelor, 10M, sang from 80 to 310 times an hour.

On March 21st 10M was eating in the trap as my all-important female approached:

"10M hurries out. They threaten each other, both somewhat puffed. He starts to drive her to the west. Where is 5M? Why doesn't he come to protect her? 10M pushes her farther and farther west; she turns to face him, but he drives her again. Here comes 5M at last! He flies to a post and sings, notices his wife and 10M, and flies near. 10M hurries away."

While both males were busy threatening each other, the lady drew near the trap and entered it! I pulled the string and rushed over in the greatest excitement. Her band read "A124094." *It was Una!* She had arrived the very same day as a year ago.

"Una is like herself in her lack of volubility," I noted, "but it is strange that she was so uninterested in the trap when much of last summer she ate there daily and had not been caught since April 15. Last year she was a very lion towards 4M, yet today she let herself be driven by 10M on her own land! She will have to unlearn Uno's songs which she so eagerly answered in 1929 and learn to respond to a new set."

10M triumphed at last by applying Danton's slogan of "Audacity, again audacity, and always audacity." By keeping everlastingly at it, he gradually wedged in a territory between 5M, Uno, and 4M, most of the fights being staged with

5M. Although he had come late upon the scene, in time he had a proper homestead to offer a bride; yet no bride appeared. He was our chief singer among the Song Sparrows day after day. Had he been too late, and would he have to sing in vain all spring and summer? Finally, on the 8th of April his song was silenced, as he looked proudly down upon a wife, whom I called Dieci. Both she and 10M were to return year after year to the scene where he had won a territory with so much energy and determination.

Every one was now happily married—Uno and Een, 4M and Chatvar, 5M and Una, 10M and Dieci, not to mention the other Song Sparrows to the south, west, and north, many of which I later came to know. The nesting season was about to begin.

CHAPTER 6

Een and the Little Snakes

IN THE lovely warm weather of mid-April, the Song Sparrows started to build. Una placed her nest under a grass tuft opposite the ash, and Een hid hers near the site of Uno's first nest the year before and his second nest the year before that. On the 20th each nest held an egg.

Chatvar had chosen a spot near the north rosebush, but her nest remained disappointingly empty. Although on the 18th it had been finished save for the lining, it was not until the 24th that I found an egg in it, and that was a Cowbird's! On this same date Een had four eggs and Una five. Two days later Chatvar's nest held two Cowbird eggs and the next day, at last, the one and only Song Sparrow egg I ever saw there; by May 6, however, this had vanished. Something was evidently helping itself to Chatvar's eggs, leaving the larger Cowbird eggs. Three days later we discovered a two-foot snake a yard from the nest; we put it in a paper bag, carried it to the river and threw it in; it promptly turned about and started for home. My small daughter and I waved the bag and shouted till it changed its course and reached the opposite bank.

Perhaps the care of two Cowbird eggs failed to arouse Chatvar's interest, or perhaps she was naturally a poor mother. At any rate she could not have incubated her charges faithfully, for it was not until May 10—at least fourteen days after the laying of the second Cowbird egg—that one infant hatched. The little thing did not thrive, and on May 13 the nest held only one addled egg, while 4M and Chatvar were busily engaged searching for a new nesting site.

Een, in the meantime, incubated her first set on much the same schedule that Una had followed the year before. On April 26th, I watched Uno and Een from five o'clock to one; in these eight hours Uno sang 415 times. Een's vacations from the nest ranged from four to nine minutes; her periods on duty were the following length: 52 minutes, 48, 28, 27, 28, 27, 29, 29, 14, 21, 32, 35, and 25. A surprising similarity was shown by the six periods between 7:30 and 10:45, but after that the charm was broken. Uno guarded the nest seven times, and once visited it for a few minutes during Een's absence. Life was more peaceful than it had been the year before; 4M pounced on Een but once, and not a single fight took place between the males.

On May 5th I had the pleasure of viewing the first babies of the season, for on that day all of Een's eggs hatched. The next day Una had three babies, and on the 7th five. I tried to watch her, but 5M proved highly uncooperative, viewing me with distrust. I found out, however, that she was feeding her children from the start, in contrast to her treatment of her first two broods the year before. Something destroyed this young family; but from their second nest the pair raised five young, and from their third nest, two. This was much better than 10M's and Dieci's record, where three attempts at nesting resulted in but two fledglings.

This season I determined to improve my technique and

study Uno and Een by means of an umbrella blind; and I constructed one of green transparent cloth as recommended in the books. It was not a success. The birds could see me better than I could them, and all three of us were unhappy. Almost the only thing I learned that I had not been able to discover from my more distant position in 1929 was the variety of soft notes used by both parents at the nest.

Uno gathered food from different parts of his territory, but Een foraged in the vicinity of the nest, discovering other creatures besides insects:

"May 7. Een attacks a medium-sized garter snake about eight feet south of the nest. I hurry out, but fail to find it.

"May 8. She is fighting a snake two yards to the west, sputtering and darting at it. It looks small to me. She is all upset, scolding her loudest with notes usually heard only after the young have left the nest: *Fit, chunk, chick, whit, chock, whilk, tip, tip, whit, chulk.* Some of these reproofs may be for the snake, but I fear that most of them are directed at me.

"May 9. Een dashes at a snake, driving it off. . . . She is pursuing a small snake without a sound; it retreats hastily. . . . She is saying *which* at a little snake just above the nest; she drives it *down right over the nest and young.* Uno is near by, but entirely oblivious to his wife's tribulations."

That Een's strenuous efforts to chase off her reptilian neighbors had not met with signal success may be inferred from an experience I had on May 10, as I sat in the blind, my hat on the ground beside me:

"A wee snake poked its head from under my hat! Tried to catch it, but it vanished."

I never had the opportunity of observing the reaction to snakes of any other Song Sparrows. The contrast in the behavior of the two birds was curious: Een's aversion and Uno's indifference, even when in 1929 a sizable individual lay coiled within two feet of Uno's babies.

Een, a devoted mother, worked so hard at feeding the children that during the last half of nest life she outshone her husband. Uno had adjusted his activities to the capabilities of his three wives, two of whom had been efficient, but the other quite the opposite. In 1928 his mate had furnished most of the meals at the start; in 1929 Uno had been almost the sole provider for his first two families; but now, with such an energetic spouse as Een, he was again taking things a bit easily. The four young left the nest on May 15th; Een did not promptly turn them over to their father, but helped to feed them until the first day of June, an exceptionally long period of maternal care.

The second nest was built in the historic rose hedge, and on June 25 three young were fledged, forty-one days after their brothers, the longest interval between successful Song Sparrow broods that I ever knew. Een was again in no hurry to start her next nest. On July 10th I noted a curious incident:

"7:10 A.M. Uno pounces on Een twice between 7:00 and 7:08; she said nothing the first time, but *zhee* the second. She has fed a child three times in the last 15 minutes. It does not beg or flutter at all.

"*Uno attacks it.* Evidently he wants to start with the third nesting, but Een is too busy with her well grown child, now 25 days old.

"5 P.M. Een is carrying food to a child, but Uno is feeding only himself."

The next day it was evident that the pair were nesting near the front of our house, since Uno gave a signal song here and Een answered him. He continued to sing in the box elder next to the veranda; but search as diligently as we would in the privet hedge, on the bank, and in and under the shrubs, we could not find the nest. On the 13th Een spent a half-hour or more down in the garden; during this time she and Uno each fed a child once.

Two days later I took a walk to North Interpont after supper:

"7:40 P.M. Uno was singing as I left the house at 7:00; to my utter astonishment I find him and Een *north of the Third Dike*—some two hundred yards from home! He comes within twelve feet of me; I throw him crumbs, and he scrambles to get them. What *are* they doing here?

"8:15. Uno is back at home, singing *C*. Een must have started nesting and been broken up. How I bless the distinctive bands that enable me to recognize the birds wherever I meet them!"

That was the last of their attempts at nesting that season. It was not until fall that we discovered Een's empty nest wonderfully concealed in the woodbine on the front porch!

CHAPTER 7

Two Divorces and a Happy Ending

WE HAVE long been led to think that most birds can be extolled as models of marital fidelity, and the belief that mating for life was the rule among them was fondly held by many people. It came as a shock, therefore, when Dr. S. Prentiss Baldwin delved into the private lives of the House Wrens on his estate in northern Ohio and announced that these birds usually change partners for the second brood in one season! After I had watched Uno and Una, 4M and Quarta in 1929, and seen how each pair stuck together through thick and thin, I was pleased to think how superior Song Sparrows were to House Wrens, whose reputation as breakers of other birds' happy homes had been bad enough before.

I had much to learn about Song Sparrows.

Having found the study of two pairs so absorbing, I was tempted to enlarge my zone of influence. Gradually I became acquainted with the neighbors of my birds, and later some of the more distant inhabitants, my chief assistant in this project being a large new automatic trap. On the 10th of April a pair of unbanded Song Sparrows that I had called the Tree Pair were driven from their home south of Dike I by a man with a plow. They attempted to settle beside the Second Dike but found no welcome here; instead, there was puffing, wing-lifting, chasing, and rapid singing. The refugees had to move on.

Nothing further in regard to this pair of birds—both unbanded—appears in my notes until May 17, when to my astonishment and chagrin I discovered an uncharted pair feeding young in a nest just north of 20M's territory and west of 26M's. I believe that they were the "Tree Pair" and that they had been able to establish themselves here quietly with comparatively little resistance, so that, busy as I was looking after so many birds, I had been unaware of their existence. In the nest were two small Song Sparrows and two fat Cowbirds. I decided to place my pull-string trap over the nest in hope of getting the parents without the trouble of training them to come to food.

This I did on the 20th, when I was shocked to find the Cowbirds the only occupants of the nest. In seventeen minutes the mother entered; I gave her a blue band, and six-year-old Janet suggested we name her Bluebell. The devoted little bird returned again and again to feed her foster children within the trap, but where was her mate? I had not seen him since the start of the experiment at 8:30 in the morning. Although I visited the nest at intervals all day, the only parent to be seen was Bluebell.

The next morning a curious thing happened. I was watching Bluebell as she labored alone, when all at once I noticed 5M, also watching her, quietly and stealthily. As she flew from the nest, he dashed after her, pounced on her, and sang, while she protested. Immediately 26M appeared on his west fence and sang. 5M turned home, being attacked on the way by 10M. 5M had had to cross some one else's territory, either

10M's or 20M's, in order to come to Bluebell's. How had he known that Bluebell's husband had deserted her? This incident proved to me that the Song Sparrows may be aware of neighborhood affairs, even two territories distant.

In the meantime there were great excitements near the end of Dike II; three different males were trying to oust a new bird that had determined to settle there. Although I can never be certain, because this bird was not banded until June, I believe that he was the Tree Male and Bluebell's mate. He could not have been much attached to this substitute territory, and he apparently was so disturbed by my placing the trap over his nest, that he simply left his wife and children and settled not two hundred yards away! He was fortunate in getting a new wife—Jet—without loss of time, for on June 1 I found her building on top of the dike, but this and the following attempt at raising families came to naught. 29M, as I named him, migrated South and returned to the same place on the Second Dike on March 20, 1931, getting a mate two days later. Jet returned March 23rd and joined 40M on Dike I.

On May 22nd Bluebell's lusty young Cowbirds left the nest. I certainly pitied her with such a load to shoulder all by herself. Her neighbors to the east—26M and Rosemary (ornamented with pink bands) were feeding a Cowbird some two days older than Bluebell's. By May 31 this Cowbird had wandered over into 4M's land, and Rosemary followed him:

"4M attacks her twice, pouncing and singing, while she tries to escape him. 26M fails to come to the rescue; just sings in his garden."

On June 3rd I wrote:

"26M is in his garden singing busily. Rosemary is in our garden feeding her great Cowbird, twice as big as she. She says *tip-tip-tip* at me, warning her precious foster child.

"Bluebell makes a touching picture with a full-grown Cowbird on each side.

"Rosemary's Cowbird hopefully begs from 4M, who merely *looks* at him."

The next day I noted:

"26M is singing sweetly on a post; a Cowbird is sitting next

Bluebell Makes a Touching Picture with a Full-grown Cowbird on Each Side

to him and begging. He leaves, finds food, and *feeds it,* not once, but twice. . . .

"26M feeds a Cowbird and is much interested in its foster mother, following her wherever she goes. *It is Bluebell.* She appears with two juicy larvae in her bill, waits a bit, searches about, but no Cowbird appearing, eats them herself. I'm glad Bluebell is having a little assistance in her burdensome task of raising two Cowbirds all by herself."

I now began to suspect a scandal in Song-Sparrowdom, as 26M was feeding *Bluebell's* Cowbirds, not his own. As for

Rosemary, I thought she might join lonely 20M, who had lost his mate in late May. Being occupied with so many pairs, I had rather lost sight of Chatvar; her second nest had been destroyed, and her third deserted after the laying of two eggs. I suddenly realized that I had not been sure of seeing her since May 29th, the day that the second egg had been laid.

On June 6th matters stood thus:

"Rosemary is still feeding her enormous Cowbird some seventeen days after it left the nest. Looks three times as big as she.

"26M is being pursued by Bluebell's two cherubs; feeds them. Bluebell is also feeding them."

I then settled down to investigate the mystery of Chatvar. After half an hour with 4M, I wrote, "Chatvar must have been killed."

So there had been two divorces. 29M had deserted Bluebell and acquired a new wife; Bluebell had accepted 26M, who had been deserted by Rosemary, who had accepted 4M after he had lost his second wife in that season! If it had not been for my putting the trap over Bluebell's nest, that pair would not have been separated; and if it had not been for Rosemary's Cowbird wandering into 4M's territory, 26M and Rosemary should have remained together. It all worked out happily in the end, however; if these shifts had not taken place, 4M might not have got a third wife.

Rosemary built herself a charming nest in the same rosebush that Quarta had chosen; she laid the first of four eggs on June 8th. Three of the eggs hatched June 22nd, the fourth the next day; three little birds left on July 1st, the fourth on the 2nd. 4M had had three wives that season; three nests had come to grief, but at length he and his third mate had raised a brood.

Bluebell's nest, however, eluded me.

It was not until June 18 that I wrote:

"My 50th Song Sparrow nest for the season! Bluebell's and 26M's under a big burdock leaf with four beautiful eggs, blue with the prettiest brown wreath at the large end. 26M *chunked* so vigorously when I came near that my suspicions were aroused."

Something destroyed this nest, and hunt as I would, I could not locate the next one. It proved to be the last found that season, my sixty-first. On July 27th as I was passing by, I saw that both parents had caterpillars in their bills; they refused to continue feeding until I withdrew and partly hid myself behind a tree. The nest was in a mass of chicken-wire, not concealed in any way, but easily overlooked as it appeared to be merely a piece of debris. In it were two young about nine days old; they left that same afternoon.

So ended the drama of these three pairs of Song Sparrows: of 29M who left his wife in the lurch, of gallant Bluebell and kindly 26M, of Rosemary and her Cowbird child, and finally of the happy ending of the season for 4M after so many misadventures.

CHAPTER 8

4M and Xantippe

IN THE spring of 1931 many of my favorites failed to return from the South—Una, Een, Bluebell, 5M, and—saddest of all—Uno. Every morning from late February through March I hopefully listened for Uno's sweet songs, but always in vain. It was a bitter disappointment to me to realize at last that never again should I welcome home this engaging personality, and never again rejoice in his clear, silvery strains.

Now that Uno was gone forever, 4M took first place in my affections. Each September I rejoiced when I first heard one of his fine songs and each October I delighted in his magnificent singing. During each winter I watched him in the vicinity of the garden, in the coldest weather associated with a little band of others of his kind. During the first warm days in late January and in February, when bats fluttered out and swamp tree frogs called, 4M remembered his songs once more, at first in an uncertain voice; but if spring stayed awhile before the inevitable return of winter, he was soon announcing with all his might the ownership of the garden.

Although most of the Song Sparrows had distressingly short

lives, by some miracle 4M lived on and on. What was the tale of his loves from 1931 through 1934?

They were four: Blueberry, 80M's Daughter, Sweetbriar, and Goldenrod. Blueberry was notable in that she rejoined 4M the second year—a rare event on Interpont, because of the high mortality of the birds and the many chances a male

During Each Winter I Watched Him in the Vicinity of the Garden

has to obtain a mate before his last year's wife arrives. Unfortunately, in 1932 Blueberry disappeared before she had completed her first set of eggs. A second mate arrived in May, a bird banded in the nest the year before; something destroyed her babies and perhaps killed her as well. Misfortune again attended 4M, for in 1933 Sweetbriar vanished before her first eggs hatched, and 4M sang in vain the rest of the season. In 1934 his luck changed; he and Goldenrod reared two young in their first nest.

4M and Xantippe

In the late winter of 1935 4M was the only old male Song Sparrow on Interpont, but a number of young residents had taken up territories in the vicinity: to the north, 225M; to the south, 220M and 223M (4M's son-in-law-to-be); and to the east, 221M. From the 9th of February on, 4M had been singing steadily, and I was having a rewarding time studying his awakening song and measuring with a photometer the light at the time of its start.

I was not pleased on March 7th to discover that a mate had arrived, for I was not ready to have my study of his singing cut short. Under the circumstances I decided to take careful notes on the wooing procedure:

"She is on a post; he suddenly flies at her, hitting into her; chases her; sings *D*. She says *eee-eee-eee*. 225M is singing constantly. She flies over in the latter's direction. 4M chases her back. . . . She is looking towards 225M's land; 4M is watching her. She flies to the brush pile with 4M after her. 4M drives her home, giving *G* as he swoops over her.

"For five minutes they are on the south side of 4M's territory, 4M constantly watching.

"225M is singing his loudest. 4M's mate works over to the north, but 4M doesn't let her out of his sight an instant. They feed near each other. 225M approaches. She gives the threat-note *jhee,* and 4M chases *him* home.

"For a short while the pair stay west of the rose hedge, she eating and chattering, he watching and singing. Twice they come to blows.

"She flies to 225M's weed patch with 4M after her. He always keeps between her and her other suitor. Now there's a battle between the males. She goes over *into* the weed patch. 4M chases her home; pounces on her and sings. Then *she* drives *him*."

This forthright courtship was dramatic to watch; but after

an hour and a half I was thoroughly chilled and had to retreat to the house. This new female did not appeal to me, I suppose because she did not seem to appreciate my dear 4M. I wondered whether she would not desert, and I rather hoped she would.

But she refused to accommodate me.

A few days later I spent a rather dull hour trying to watch the pair. There was one amusing incident:

"4M and his mate are feeding across the road south of the ash. 4M flies home and sings a *J* series, but she stays. Soon 220M approaches. She greets him with an emphatic *jhee,* hunching her shoulders and puffing herself up. Nevertheless he comes nearer and nearer. She hurries home to 4M *jhee*ing loudly. 4M rushes at 220M and routs him. She chatters and chatters, then *chunks* and *chunks.*"

I was trying to repeat on 4M and his mate what I had done six years before with Uno and Una, but it was discouraging work. This pair ranged over twice the area of the other, frequently going out of sight in the great weed patch by the big maple, and foraging independently of each other. Uno and Una had been charming together, affectionate, vocal, and responsive to each other. But this female was a cold, old-maidish creature, tyrannizing over her fine husband like a veritable Xantippe. I did not wonder that he avoided her. And one day I found Goldenrod, his pleasant wife of the year before, with an unbanded mate near the river. If only she had returned a little earlier!

I resolved to kidnap Xantippe for a while, for I needed more data on 4M's singing, and I hoped he might in the meantime get an agreeable wife. But no matter how alluringly I prepared the traps she declined to go near them.

4M was more accommodating:

"10:00 A.M. 4M is in the flat trap with a female English

Sparrow. He gives no alarm note as I come, but refuses to be shooed into the gathering cage. I wave and wave the black cloth, while English Sparrow rushes back and forth distractedly. At last he goes into the cage. He has lost the white band I made and gave him six years ago.

"3:00 P.M. 4M in the trap again! And I had just been telling the family of his intelligence! Xantippe is still unbanded after nearly a month."

On April 4, to my surprise, I found a pair of Song Sparrows established in 5M's old territory; the male was 221M, a bird that had been somewhat of a puzzle to me. He had stayed around our house, sleeping in the spruce just east of us, and although he had given the awakening song normally, I had never heard him sing in the daytime. In early March he had been driven from his sleeping quarters by the return of a last year's summer resident, 204M, and I had seen nothing of him since. Yet here he was next to 4M, peacefully in possession of both land and wife.

Before long I caught 221M's mate; I gave her yellow bands and named her Dandelion. As she flew from the study window, she alighted in the garden and Xantippe attacked her. It occurred to me that here was my chance to catch that tiresome creature; when Dandelion next entered the trap, I placed it with her inside in the middle of 4M's land, a device that had been successful with other birds. Again I was disappointed. 4M hopped on top of the trap, rather puffed out, but Xantippe was indifferent.

On April 10th, 4M and his wife were occupied in building play, picking up large loads and flying with them:

"The pair stay together rather closely now; one follows the other. 4M watches her a good deal, while she drives him in an ill tempered sort of way. She is the most shrewish female I ever studied.

"4M pounces on 204M's wife. 204M drives him home. He sings *A*, standing at bay on a little elm."

Victory came at last. Three days later an angry Xantippe was inside the four-cell trap that I had purchased particularly for the capture of Cowbirds. She struggled the most and bit the hardest of any Song Sparrow I ever dealt with. Unfortunately it was now too late to carry out my plan, for experiments at this stage might easily have left 4M without any wife at all.

On April 20th a great event took place: Xantippe started to build! She had chosen a spot in the raspberry patch, where Chatvar had constructed her third nest five years earlier. Not that she showed any great enthusiasm, for she carried but ten loads in the hour that I watched from eight to nine.

The next morning I settled myself with high hopes on a bit of cement wall by the woodshed. I stayed there *three and a half hours* in the vain expectation that something might happen. She picked up six loads, dropped four and carried two to her nest. I heartily echoed the lament of Edmund Selous: "How barren is this watching! How little does it lead to!"

For the next week Xantippe seemed to forget all about her nest. On the 23rd I found her and 4M calling on the 221s. Dandelion was building in the ditch by the ash; 4M pounced on her while her poor husband was in the trap. Next, 4M pounced on 225M's wife. A bit later the 4s were having a boundary quarrel with 221M, and the curious thing was that Xantippe was more bellicose than her husband, again and again threatening her humble neighbor. Usually there is a sex division in these encounters, males meeting males and females, females. Although Xantippe showed herself unfeminine in this and other respects, yet I never heard her sing. Since my recording of Una's poor attempts at song in 1929,

I had heard females sing only occasionally, except for two birds that gave whole series of squeaky refrains; one of these was more aggressive than her mate in the defense of their territory, while the other showed but slight interest in her nest.

Dandelion worked away industriously at her nest, which was safely hidden under an old newspaper. Once 4M pounced on her and 221M failed to come. The next time he was just about to pounce, and she objected strenuously *jhee jhee*. This time 221M came to investigate, and the males puffed themselves out; but 221M was plainly in awe of his domineering neighbors to the east. Obliging little Dandelion in the meantime showed herself most cooperative by entering the trap every day and giving me the data I needed on changes in weight of a bird in the different stages of egg laying and incubating.

On the 29th of April something happened:

"Wonder of wonders, Xantippe gets a load of material! At last she is lining her nest. Takes two loads in one hour, a great achievement for her.

"4M sang 167 times. He sings far more than any other Song Sparrow on Interpont."

Unfortunately, on May 1st the neighbors' handy man weeded the raspberries and pulled up a thistle which had sheltered the nest. I replaced it, but in its withered state it afforded small protection; and I feared Xantippe would have nothing more to do with her nest, in which at best her interest had never been more than lukewarm.

Notwithstanding the changed state of affairs, on the 3rd of May *Xantippe laid her first egg,* thirteen days after she had started to build. The next day there was another, but on the 5th there were only two eggs, the second having disappeared. The prospect was not any too cheerful.

On May 6 disaster had overtaken this nest as it had so many others of 4M's. Two punctured eggs in a deserted nest! It was evidently the work of House Wrens. Up to now these potentially dangerous little creatures had been peaceable denizens of our garden; perhaps it was the exposure of the nest that had led to its destruction.

Never again did I lay eyes on Xantippe. I believe when she found her nest disturbed she simply left. In a way, I was not sorry to have seen the last of her, but my plans for making a detailed study of 4M's nesting behavior had certainly been wrecked.

CHAPTER 9

4M Charms His Neighbor's Wife

FROM earliest dawn 4M was singing gloriously every day. For years I had wanted to count the number of times a Song Sparrow would sing throughout a whole day. Now at last the way seemed clear, and on Saturday May 11th I started on the undertaking.

Vega, Arcturus, and Jupiter shone down on me as I came out into the garden at 4:42; Wood Thrushes and Robins were already singing, and a Catbird was mewing. Two minutes later 4M began with *D*. The Catbird sang, and the next minute 225M answered 4M, while a Mourning Dove uttered his peaceful coo. At 4:51 a House Wren chittered, and at 4:55 I heard the *witchery witchery* of a Maryland Yellowthroat; at 5:02 I recorded the first White-crowned Sparrow, and at 5:05 a Goldfinch's happy song. The next minute a Yellow Warbler gave his simple lay. At 5:07 there was a Starling's whistle, and six minutes later came the yap of English Sparrows. 4M, in the meantime, sang steadily at the rate of five songs a minute. It was not until 5:50—thirty minutes after sunrise—that he paused for thirty-five seconds to snatch his first bite of breakfast, taking another little snack four minutes later.

My breakfast and lunch were served to me out-of-doors by the children, while I recorded every song in every minute. Until noon this indefatigable bird sang almost continuously, giving from 200 to 278 songs an hour. The next three hours he dropped to an average of 150 songs, and after that he rested, singing but little during late afternoon and evening. The last song came at 7:43—seven minutes after sunset. It was the two thousand three hundred and fifth!

Happy with my success in this undertaking, I decided to test my birds with a stuffed Song Sparrow. Some birds will mistake a specimen for a modest female and court it. A friend had given me a mounted Song Sparrow, and this I fastened on top of the trap in the garden. 4M sang on regardless, and it was not until a half-hour had passed that he dropped down to investigate. He pecked the stuffed bird once, then flew away. He gave me the impression that he was too clever a bird to be fooled by a dummy.

It was different with 221M when Stuffy was fixed under the ash. He hopped about it with feathers fluffed, then flew to the branch above and sang softly. Then down he came, all puffed out, faced the enemy, and tried to fight it, attacking it breast to breast and pecking it on the head.

The bird that was most incensed over this unaccountable visitor was 204M, when he found it standing on top of the bank above his nest. Puffed out into the shape of a ball, his left wing held erect and rapidly vibrating, he sang continuously, *sotto voce*. When the insulting creature failed to respond in any manner, he attacked it again and again—still singing—pecking poor Stuffy's head so savagely that I had to hasten to the rescue.

The presence of a silent, motionless Song Sparrow could

only be interpreted by these birds as a male dominating a territory; so even though 221M and 204M were in the middle of their own territories they both assumed at the outset the role of the challenger. When this brought no results, the next recourse was to repel the intruder, and this they had done with fury.

Two days after I had taken 4M's all-day conversation, the 221s' four babies hatched. On May 22nd, when I visited the

204M Fights Stuffy

family, I found that two had left the nest; father and mother were greatly excited, and, curiously enough, 4M showed sympathy with their distress, exclaiming *tit-tit-tit-tit*. During the next few days I was busy at my desk and spent little time with the birds except for making the daily rounds of the nests and noting that 4M was still devoting the better part of each day to music.

On the 28th there was a change. My notebook reads:

"4M sings very little today. It was over three weeks ago that his wife deserted him. I went out to visit him, but retreated before the armies of mosquitoes.

"May 29. 8:00 A.M. 4M sings only a little. Do not see him, but Dandelion is scolding on the Bluebird box in his land.

"10:30. 4M has barely sung at all. Is it the rain, or fatigue, or is there a lady on the horizon? Has a new bird arrived, or could he be engaged to 221M's mate! I must investigate.

"Go into the garden, but the mosquitoes are unbelievably vicious. 4M is on the brush pile, apparently much interested in Dandelion's activities."

The next day I braved the tormentors and stayed in the garden with the birds. It was soon plain that 4M was a married man once more, and that his wife was none other than his next-door neighbor Dandelion! Her deserted husband was caring for one child near the ash, while the gay little lady was feeding two children—one in the rose hedge and one by the big maple—and making love to 4M besides. He was following her hither and yon and occasionally bestowing a morsel on the stepchildren.

How I wished I had seen the beginning of the love affair! Evidently one of the young birds had come into 4M's land, and 4M had wooed and won the mother under the very eyes of her husband! Once before, 4M had found a wife in this way when Rosemary followed her Cowbird into his land. In this case, however, as in two others I knew of, there had been some space—at least a hundred feet—between the boundaries of the two territories. Perhaps 221M's meek nature had had something to do with this divorce.

On May 31 Dandelion was busier than ever, for today she was making herself a nest in the north rosebush where two other mates of 4M had built, Quarta six years before and Rosemary five years. Four days later she laid her first egg. On this day I found her and one of her children dashing about in the trap, the little one saying *geek, geek*. 4M was greatly disturbed as I transferred them to the gathering cage, coming near and uttering a curious note—*pooh, pooh, pooh,* then starting to sing as I took them into the house. This was his way, I suppose, of trying to call his mate back. Upon my return with the captives in the cage, 4M stopped his song at once and gave his fear note. The rest of that day and the next, whenever any of us entered the garden, he greeted us with an emphatic *tit-tit-tit.* I never saw this child of Dandelion's again, but two others were in their father's care on the 8th of June.

4M had a wife again, but little good would it do me, since an imperative engagement in Massachusetts in late June would take me away just when the babies were due to hatch. What could be done? Somewhere I had read how some one had taken a Song Sparrow's newly laid eggs and given her some well-incubated ones of a Yellow-breasted Chat and of how pleased the foster parents had been. The 185s' eggs were nearly ready to hatch; on June 7 I exchanged them with Dandelion's fresh set. Friends were skeptical: "She will kill such premature young." I rigged up a canvas blind by Dandelion's nest and eagerly awaited events. I planned to make a careful study of the nest life of the birds, and a fellow ornithologist had promised to take photographs, both moving and still, of 4M caring for babies.

Late in the afternoon of June 9th the first baby hatched. I slipped into the blind while 4M's attention was elsewhere, and cautiously peered through the slit. There sat Dandelion the very picture of content. Apparently she accepted the extraordinary precocity of her children with the utmost calm. She yawned, then pecked at something and ate it, and soon slipped off. In nine minutes she was back and gently fed a small insect to the baby, mincing the food into tiny fragments.

I made a slight noise against the sow thistle that shared the blind with me; up came her head instantly. Then she preened herself, rose and looked beneath her, shook her feathers, and settled down. Presently she caught a mosquito and ate it—noble deed. At 5:27 she stood up and ate eggshell. Baby Number Two had hatched.

I returned again after supper and had a happy time watching Dandelion's tender care of her foster babies. 4M apparently knew nothing of the astonishing happenings in his household; he sang a good deal and twice guarded the nest during his mate's absences. She fed the infants seven times in three hours.

The next morning I was out early, eager to continue the charming story of mother care and to see 4M's devotion to the babies. It was not to be. The nest was overturned and its contents gone. What vicissitudes attended the Song Sparrows and my study of them! This was a major calamity, for it was now too late to make a second exchange.

The birds were not discouraged; the next day Dandelion was building in a tangle of bedstraw west of the big maple with 4M proudly watching her. On the 15th she laid her first egg. Fate was again against them, for an overzealous gardener, not knowing of the nest, cleared out the weeds and laid the nest bare. The next day the only new egg was a Cowbird's. I hope 4M and Dandelion had better luck with the fourth attempt! Of his seventeen nests in the eight years that I knew him, only five had been successful and only thirteen young had been fledged.

As for their eggs that had been given to the neighbors, I regret to say that they had not prospered. 185M's mate incubated for four days after the first of her own eggs had hatched; after that I could find neither her nor her mate. In the fall, however, 185M was present on his territory. I suppose that when no babies appeared at the proper time, the pair may have deserted, although another Song Sparrow in Columbus sat on addled eggs for twenty-four days—twice the normal period.

Once again 4M's sweet songs welcomed us home in September. This fall—and the same had been true in 1934—he did not show the abounding energy of earlier years, and he sang but little. The last song I ever heard from him was on Thanksgiving Day. 4M, who had surmounted difficulties and dangers for so many years, at last fell a victim to some enemy.

Dr. Erwin Stresemann of Berlin once sent his regards to 4M, adding, "May he reach a Biblical age!" And this he did, if we reckon in terms of most small birds' lives. Of my banded breeding Song Sparrows, seventy-six were recorded for two years, twenty-four for three years, eight for four years, one (10M) for five years, one for six years, and 4M for eight years. I wish I knew just how old 4M lived to be. Since he was in possession of a territory in 1928, he could not have been less than eight and a half years old by December, 1935. When I first came to Columbus in the fall of 1927, I was interested in all cases of Song Sparrow warbling that I heard, and recorded every instance; there was none heard in our garden that fall and winter. Either 4M must have outgrown his warbling stage in some other place and moved into our grounds in the early spring of 1928 as a yearling bird, or he was already a year or more old in 1927, in which case he would have been at least nine and a half years old at the time of his death. A few banded song birds have been known to reach the age of ten years—Wren Tit, Purple Finch, House Finch, and Mockingbird—while a Cardinal lived to be more than thirteen years old.

4M had eleven wives during the eight years I knew him: an unbanded bird in 1928; Quarta in 1929; Quatre, Chatvar, and Rosemary in 1930; Blueberry in 1931 and 1932; 80M's

Daughter later in 1932; Sweetbriar in 1933; Goldenrod in 1934; and Xantippe and Dandelion in 1935. Seven times he had been left a widower, and only once did he have the same mate two years in succession. Goldenrod returned one year, and Rosemary two years; but each time 4M was already mated on their arrival.

When I first studied the Song Sparrows my interests were so centered on Uno that I had looked upon 4M as a truculent, meddlesome neighbor; but one day when I moved my campstool west of the rose hedge I discovered him to be a delightful bird, spirited, an accomplished songster and a devoted father. During the early years he was an overbearing individual, dominating the Song Sparrows on all sides of him; but by 1932 he was much less prone to pick quarrels, having settled down into sedate middle age.

That he was intelligent was shown by his ignoring the mounted Song Sparrow, and also, I believe, by the fact of his long survival. Although trusting towards me, he must have been cautious in the presence of strangers, and especially alert in escaping danger.

One of his most notable traits was his prowess in singing. Spring after spring I noted, "4M sings more than any other Song Sparrow on Interpont." This was especially true in fall when many of the resident birds failed to sing at all. For years, on pleasant October days 4M would sing gloriously for hours at a time, the picture of abounding energy and joy in living.

For seven years I had devoted myself to the study of Song Sparrows. During the seasons of alternating hope and discouragement, fulfillment and bitter disappointment, there had been one great blessing—the dauntless cheer of this precious bird and the miracle of his long life.

CHAPTER 10

The Grandchildren of Uno and 4M

EACH season I had banded as many Song Sparrow babies in the nest as I could, the number one year passing the hundred mark. The babies, once grown, did not come back to their exact birthplace and enter the trap in our garden, as did some amiable members of their species in New England. I had to go forth to find them. The first discovery was that of Uno's and Una's daughter, nesting with 13M some two hundred yards from home. The next year there were no fewer than seven young resident males, banded on the right leg, sprinkled all over Interpont and even beyond its borders.

Tracking my banded young took me farther and farther afield, and trapping them to discover their identity often resulted in the capture of their mates and neighbors; so gradually I extended my interests over a larger and larger area. After I had learned the language and customs of Song Sparrows and had come to know intimately a few individuals, I became fired with ambition to discover what took place among the inhabitants on the whole of Interpont. I had begun this enterprise in the spring of 1930; for four more years I worked on it, mapping and trapping, exploring the territories for the nests, and recording the vital statistics of the population.

Up and down Interpont I tramped in sunshine, rain, and snow, grieving over the untimely death of many a bird, exulting in the return of another or the discovery of some particularly well hidden nest. Though difficulties and disappointments were great, the rewards were greater. Interpont brought me deep satisfaction and keen adventure.

To my great delight, a grandson of Uno, 50M, turned up in our garden in September, 1930; he and his grandfather must have often seen and heard each other that fall, but I fear that it was only I who knew the relationship. 50M proved to be an all-year resident. In the winter he associated in our garden with 4M and other Song Sparrows, and in his first February quarreled with his ancestral rival over territory matters. He established his territory just south of our house, including part of his grandfather's estate. Twice he nested in the very woodbine where Uno's last nest had been built. In 1931 and again two years later I had the proud privilege of banding great-grandchildren of my beloved Uno; but to my disappointment I never found any of them in later years.

Una had another grandson, 95M, son of 55M, son of 5M. Una and 5M were both summer residents, but their son and grandson were permanent residents. 55M nested on North Interpont; although twelve days younger than 50M he was the latter's uncle. 95M did not have a successful life; one leg hung broken and useless, and his handsome wife deserted him.

4M lived for so many years that one would expect his descendants to have made up a fair share of the population of Interpont. This, however, was not the case, so far as I am aware. Unfortunately in 1929 his brood of four left the nest without bands, and only the single baby in the last nest was marked. Neither this bird nor any of Rosemary's four children raised the next year were found after they left the nest.

During the next five years 4M raised but four young while I was on Interpont, although in all probability more little birds were fledged later in three of the seasons. One child from each of the two successful nests survived to adulthood. Blueberry's son nested a third of a mile from home for two years; he was a resident, and his songs were all different from

Out in the World

those of his father. On May 24, 1932, I had the pleasure of banding 4M's two grandchildren; but, to my regret, I never saw them after they left the nest.

In the early spring of 1935 I was very happy to welcome 4M's daughter to 50M's former territory, not sixty feet from her birthplace. Like her father and half-brother she was a resident, although her mother was migratory. Her husband, 223M, was also a resident. She built her nest in a lattice and astonished me by laying some of the largest Song Sparrow eggs I ever measured, although she herself was a small bird. Once again disaster befell a particularly cherished bird; 4M's and Goldenrod's daughter was killed by a neighbor's cat.

In two other family lines besides Uno's and Una's I knew of grandchildren that returned and nested; but never did I find a great-grandchild of any of my Song Sparrows as a breeding bird. The reasons were two. Since I shouldered this great undertaking alone, I could not possibly find all the nests of all the birds in whom I was interested; nor could I usually carry observations throughout the whole nesting season. The other reason was the fate of Interpont.

This pleasant place of some forty acres reached its height of prosperity in March, 1932, with the population at its peak —sixty-nine pairs of Song Sparrows (all, by heroic efforts, banded)—while Interpont itself was a lovely tangle of luxuriant weeds and elder bushes. This happy state of affairs was not to last. Three misfortunes befell the Song Sparrows that season: a cold April that delayed the start of nesting, a drought in May that reduced the insect supply, and a veritable plague of Cowbirds. The next spring an unseasonable flood covered most of the nests.

These setbacks could have been endured, and when conditions were favorable again, the Song Sparrows could have multiplied once more. But in the spring of 1933 Interpont was taken over for gardens for the unemployed. Much as I regretted this, I felt it had to be; but the inexcusable destruction of trees, shrubs, and weeds along the dikes and river banks was an example of stupidity that has been only too common of late years. The Song Sparrows with few places to nest and little cover to protect them from their enemies, dwindled to a pitiful remnant.

In the days when cover was adequate and the birds were relatively undisturbed, over sixty per cent of my nesting males had survived from one year to the next and a breeding Song Sparrow lived on the average for two and a half years. In later years, however, the average life of those birds that reached maturity was only one and three-tenths years! It is no wonder that family lines became extinct.

The Song Sparrow is well able to stand rigors of climate and to keep up its numbers despite natural enemies, provided it has sufficient cover for shelter for itself and its young. But when cats and rats are added to the list of predators, and its brushy, weedy haunts are demolished in the interest of "neatness," the odds are too great.

Let us look at the humble beauty of waste places not with prejudice but enlightenment. "How rich," wrote Thoreau of his Massachusetts haunts, "like what we love to read of South American forests, is the scenery of this river! What luxuriance of weeds, what depths of mud along its sides!"

Indeed, weeds were one of the glories of Interpont—the giant ragweeds that towered above one's head, the thistles that offered snug homes to Goldfinches, the incredible cow parsnips in May, the asters and goldenrods that wove bright patterns along the ditches. Despised by many, weeds are in reality an important element in our landscape, holding the precious soil, providing nesting places for many birds, extending hospitality to migrating hosts of native sparrows that feed upon their seeds and to warblers that find upon them a harvest of insects, and finally affording food and shelter to those hardy birds that brave the northern winter. Let us therefore leave weeds and shrubs and tangled vines wherever we can along roadsides and fence rows, for where such things are, there will birds be also.

CHAPTER 11

Curious Ways of the Cowbird

THE "unaccountable practice" of the "Cowpen Bunting" (as the bird was sometimes called) "of dropping its eggs into the nests of other birds . . . thus entirely abandoning its progeny to the care and mercy of strangers," caused Alexander Wilson a hundred years ago to marvel over the amazing "works of the great Creator." Apropos of the fact that the baby Cowbird usually hatches before its nestmates, he wrote: "In this singular circumstance, we see a striking provision of the Deity" for the maintenance of the species. Later writers might wonder why the Deity should trouble himself over so perverse a creature, but this was not the attitude of the Father of American Ornithology. In mentioning the "singular–I will not say unnatural–conduct of the European Cuckoo" he declines to attempt to "account for this remarkable habit, . . . far less to consider as an error what the wisdom of heaven has imposed as a duty on the species."

Near the end of the nineteenth century, Wilson's quaint piety had been forgotten and righteous indignation had taken its place. The Cowbird is "an acknowledged villain" with "no standing in the bird world," "the pariah of birddom," whose "deeds are evil." As for the female, her "thoroughly despicable nature" is "lacking in every moral and maternal instinct." Nowadays, most writers on birds are less reproachful, but a gentleman from the Middle West in 1933 offered the following reflections on the parasitic behavior of this species:

"I wonder if this habit of the Cowbird is the reason why the other birds have nothing to do with him, and I wonder if this is why Cowbirds do not sing? . . . Perhaps it is because they do not have the joy of caring for their little ones."

Cowbirds belong to the blackbird family; their relatives are Red-winged Blackbirds, Bobolinks, Orioles, and Meadowlarks—all of them normal parents and some of them builders of elaborate nests. The origin of the parasitic habit in the Cowbird has caused much speculation. Into this subject I will not venture except to mention the suggestion of that grand old naturalist Otto Widmann, since it reminds us of early conditions of life of this species:

"There are two peculiarities for which our Cowbird is renowned: the one which gives him his scientific name Molothrus, a parasite; the other which causes him to be called Cowbird, his strong attachment to grazing animals especially horses and cattle. Now, should there not be a connection between these two traits? Nobody would think that the habit of following horses and cattle has been formed since the introduction of these animals by the white man. Its Indian name Buffalo-bird was certainly no misnomer and it can hardly be questioned that for ages the buffalo, or American bison, was the animal which, in the economy of our Cowbird, played the part now taken by the domestic animals."

He then suggests that the habit might have arisen in past ages in Cowbirds in both North and South America in connection with the ancestors of present-day horses.

"As the pastoral habit of the bird became stronger, it gave

rise to the parasitic habit, simply because, in following the roving animals, the bird often strayed from home too far to reach its nest in time for the deposition of the egg, and being hard pressed, had to look about for another bird's nest wherein to lay the egg."

On Interpont the Cowbird is an important member of the bird community, and particularly important to the most abundant bird there—the Song Sparrow. It is hard to think what the Cowbird would do but for his chief victim that raises the bulk of his children. As for the Song Sparrows, although they detest grown-up Cowbirds, yet they cheerfully —and all unknowingly—rear the little Cowbirds as if they were their own children.

How Song Sparrows starting with housekeeping for the first time realize that this species is an enemy, has puzzled me. 221M, for instance, known to be a young bird from the warbling character of his song in the winter, was greatly disturbed over the courting parties of Cowbirds in his ash tree early in the season before nesting had begun. Once I saw 4M and Quarta fly at and rout a Cowbird in the presence of one of their five-weeks-old children; perhaps this may be the way that some young Song Sparrows learn to distrust Cowbirds.

The Oven-bird, however, according to Dr. H. W. Hann, does not recognize the Cowbird as a menace to its welfare.

Cowbirds are highly socialized beings; not only in the late summer, fall, and winter do they flock together, but even in the breeding season friendliness flourishes. This very trait was one of the reproaches brought against them by the older writers.

"After an observance of many years," wrote Dr. Potter to Alexander Wilson, "I could never discover anything like *pairing,* or a mutual attachment between the sexes. . . . When the female separates from the company, her departure is not noticed; no gallant partner accompanies her, nor manifests any solicitude in her absence; nor is her return greeted by that gratulatory tenderness that so eminently characterizes the males of other birds. The male proffers the same civilities to any female, indiscriminately, and they are reciprocated accordingly, without exciting either resentment or jealousy in any of the party."

That some Cowbirds, however, are eminently respectable was discovered by Dr. Herbert Friedmann, who tells us in his monograph that at Ithaca, New York, "each male and female has a definite territory" and that "there is more or less definite pairing between the birds." On Interpont, on the contrary, with an abundance of Cowbirds, casual observations appeared to confirm the views of the older writers. Each bird —male or female—usually ranges over about twenty acres, but the Song Sparrow nests on each twenty acres are regularly parasitized by two female Cowbirds and occasionally by one or two others. Indeed, two females often hunt about in the grass side by side in the friendliest manner imaginable.

It was through marking with colored bands the thirteen Cowbirds that entered my traps, that I endeavored to get light on the monogamous—or other—tendencies of my birds. In 1932 the male Pinko was seen with all three banded females —Pinkee, Reddee, and Bluee—and two unbanded females besides. A single female might be attended by any number of males from one up to five.

Reddee I believed to be the mother of the most beautiful Cowbird eggs on Interpont; they were white and shining and adorned with tiny brown and lavender spots. I first caught her on North Interpont in April, 1932, and placed her in the cloth-covered carrying cage with a male Song Sparrow—141M. About halfway home he apparently became terrified over his traveling companion and screeched continually *wheech,*

wheech, wheech, exciting all the Song Sparrows that we passed; out of the weeds they came, crests raised and tails spread.

After that Reddee often appeared in my notes:

"May 18, 10:20. Pinko and three unbanded males are

The Male Cowbird Displays

courting Reddee. All dart down to 125M's land; Reddee instantly disappears in the grass. A fifth male joins the group on the weeds and they bow and display to one another just as to a female. They first point their bills directly up, then fluff out their feathers, arch their necks and spread their tails, giving a squeaky *tsee;* they raise their wings and start to topple forward, but right themselves just in time. A pair of

Maryland Yellowthroats are much distressed. . . . 125M scolds, while the Yellowthroats become more and more unhappy.

"10:34. Reddee appears 150 feet west of where she entered. All the males rush to her. She walks ahead to the west; they display before her. She chatters and flies west followed by her troop of suitors.

"May 25. Reddee and an unbanded male are in the new garden. She suddenly threatens her escort who squeals and dodges. Another male now alights in a near-by tree; Reddee's companion follows and threatens him, making him move a foot or two."

The next year I was pleased to have Reddee return, and once again I found the distinctive "marbled" eggs on her territory. Although usually appearing indifferent to her admirers, one day she seemed distinctly annoyed:

"Reddee is in 5M's ash; a male comes and displays. She goes for him again and again, pecking him fiercely and causing him to lose his balance and descend to lower branches."

Pinkee and Scarlet also returned for a second year, while Bluee and Ochre were present three years; but none of the four banded males returned.

The amiable nature of the Cowbirds is shown by the rarity of quarrels among them; indeed, Dr. Friedmann never saw his birds fight. On Interpont, however, I witnessed five of these episodes, all in early April. Two of them were particularly amusing:

"Four males and two females are in 5M's ash; the males court frantically. Two separate out in a battle, clenching and falling to the ground; then one chases the other over towards the river. He returns and attacks one of the remaining males. The females leave, and their suitors follow.

"Four males are displaying before a female; another male hurries to join them. The female flies and two males follow her. One male displays to the other two; one of these pecks him, and the two fall fighting."

Not only does Madame Cowbird lay her eggs in the nests of other birds; she often removes an egg of her host. I have seen this happen twice; in 1928 from 4M's nest (the thief eating the egg and shell), and in 1934 in my first nest of the season—indeed, I was indebted to the lady Cowbird for showing it to me.

Cowbird eggs as a rule are covered with fine brown spots, and almost always are larger than those of their hosts. Twice, however, I have been surprised to have what I took to be a Song Sparrow's egg hatch into a white-plumed Cowbird instead of the black-downed Song Sparrow I had expected.

At the age of nine or ten days the young Cowbird is normally well covered with feathers and ready to step out of the nest. By chance I discovered a use for these fat boarders; when a seven- to ten-day bird is put into a trap next the nest, the foster parent will usually enter to feed it. I even hit upon the scheme of lending a little Cowbird for a day or two, or even an hour or two, to families that were without them; such visitors proving equally attractive as bait. (One of the Song Sparrows I caught in this way was Sweetbriar, the year before she became 4M's mate.) Evidently Song Sparrow parents do not know their small young personally, but will respond to the bright throat and begging notes of almost any little bird in or—later—near the nest.

During seven years' study on Interpont, 98 of the 223 Song Sparrow nests located contained Cowbird eggs; 69 held one egg, 26 held two eggs and three held three. Only once did I find four Cowbird eggs in a single nest; this happened in June, 1928, and the nest belonged to a Maryland Yellowthroat. I took the Cowbird eggs into the house at 8:23 in the morning and left them until 1:30; I then opened one, and to my dismay the infant flapped its forepaws and opened its bill! It was absolutely naked and looked more like a reptile than a bird. Another egg held a similar horrid object, but the others were fresh. I had intended doing a kind deed to the warbler, but she failed to appreciate my motives; finding such a radical change in her household, she promptly deserted her own two eggs.

A myth has grown up in regard to the incubation period of the Cowbird—"only ten days," "about the shortest period of any of our passerine birds." On Interpont with the Song Sparrow as host the Cowbird egg has *never* hatched in ten days. Sometimes it hatches in eleven days, sometimes in twelve, and occasionally in thirteen or even fourteen days. It requires about one day less of incubation than the Song Sparrow egg, hence it normally hatches first and the bird gets an advantage from the start. Some eggs have been laid after incubation has started; these have hatched from one to five days later than the Song Sparrows, and most of the little birds perished.

The young European Cuckoo will not suffer any other occupant of the nest—egg or baby bird; it humps itself up and pushes out all other objects, thus remaining the sole recipient of its foster parents' care. Little Cowbirds, on the other hand, have no instinct to eject their nestmates, and are peaceable members of the household; but their larger size sometimes brings disaster to the younger of their hosts' children. Song Sparrows often raise all of their own young that hatch along with a pensioner, anywhere from one to five Song Sparrows having been fledged in such nests. With two Cowbirds of like age in the nest, the Song Sparrows have been able to bring up only one or two of their own children. Smaller birds undoubtedly suffer more than do Song Sparrows, but there is little information on this subject. Once I found a nest containing three young Maryland Yellowthroats and a Cowbird just ready to leave.

Many writers assert that each Cowbird is raised at the expense of a brood of young. This is not true with Song Sparrows. Sixty-six successful nests without Cowbirds on Interpont raised an average of 3.4 Song Sparrows, while twenty-eight successful nests with Cowbirds averaged 2.4 Song Sparrows. So, taken by and large, each Cowbird was reared at the expense of one Song Sparrow. Early in the study when Cowbirds were not over numerous, I felt that the Song Sparrows could shoulder the load fairly easily, but in later years when the number of Song Sparrows dwindled, and the Cowbird population remained about the same, the parasite became a heavy burden to the Song Sparrow.

Strangely enough, although Cowbirds have none of the ties to eggs and young of most other birds, nevertheless they possess an uncanny ability to find their way home from astonishing distances. William Lyon of Waukegan, Illinois, has experimented with Blue Jays, Red-winged Blackbirds, Bronzed Grackles and Cowbirds, and finds that the last are his best homers; indeed, they are much better than Homing Pigeons. He has sent male Cowbirds 80, 500, 1,200, and even 2,000 miles, and some of them have always turned up again in his garden.

Two Cowbirds of which we have records made engaging pets. A "little hen Cowbird that had its liberty at all times in a suite of rooms, was tempted" by her master, F. L. Rand of St. Louis, with an array of nests containing candy eggs; she laid 13 eggs in 14 days, and "oftentimes the candy egg would be found on the floor." The other pet was a male, and the owner, R. J. O'Neal, who also lived in St. Louis, wrote, "Never have I seen a bird that was quite so companionable and happy as Chips."

Curious Ways of the Cowbird

An immense literature has gathered around the European Cuckoo; but with the exception of Dr. Friedmann's book little has been written on our American brood parasite except instances of so many eggs found in such and such nests. The Cowbird is an extraordinarily interesting bird and a careful study of its life history would provide the student with no end of fascinating problems.[1]

[1] Since this book was written a number of papers on Cowbirds have been published. The most significant of these is the notable paper "Cowbird Behavior" by Amelia R. Laskey, 1950, *Wilson Bulletin,* 62(4):157-174, based on three seasons of study at her home in Nashville, Tennessee, on Cowbirds, twenty-nine of which were color banded. Mrs. Laskey ascertained that the most elaborate displays of the males were directed as intimidation to other males; that courtship consisted in less pronounced bows and posturings and in guarding the female from other males. Copulations were observed only between the dominant male and female of a group. She found the species monogamous, although members of both sexes fed and flew together. She "observed no evidence of true territorial behavior"; she called the area occupied by the dominant pair its "domain."

It seems as if the gatherings together of my Cowbirds that I called "courting parties" must have been largely concerned with maintaining dominance relations between the males.———M.M.N.

CHAPTER 12

The Nest in the Juniper

PERCHED on the tippety-top of a red cedar, his little head bright blue in the sunshine, his breast a brilliant yellow splashed with black stripes, my Magnolia Warbler looked up to heaven and sang with all his might. *Weechy weech* was the burden of his song, given six or seven times a minute for hours at a time. This being interpreted meant: "This is my territory. Other males beware!"

Another song, that seemed to express a less serious mood, was the pretty *sing sweet,* heard in the evening and early morning, usually as the warbler flitted about feeding in the pitch and white pine grove to the west of the house at Grey Rocks, in Pelham, Massachusetts. It was this song that led to my discovery of the nest, the finding of which had been my chief ornithological ambition for the summer of 1925, for my friend Edward H. Forbush, Massachusetts State Ornithologist, had expressed surprise that this species should summer in this vicinity. Usually, he had observed, it nested in spruce, and there are no spruce trees at Grey Rocks.

Sing sweet was a new song to me, and, on hearing it the evening of June 18th, I went in search of its author. What should I see but a female Magnolia Warbler with nesting material in her beak!

"She dives into a white pine. I wait and see the performance repeated, the male in the meantime singing, but not coming into sight. Finally a little bird comes rustling out of the juniper nearest to me. After that apparently the warblers went to sleep, but the mosquitoes did not."

The next morning I examined this juniper branch and *there* was the half-built nest! It was entirely hidden from sight, and the only opening was to the north. Six days later it held three creamy little eggs splotched with hazel, chestnut, and lavender.

All went serenely, with little lady taking charge of the eggs, and her mate devoting most of the daylight hours to song; but on July 2nd a visitor arrived. Early in the morning I heard *weechy weechy weechip* south of the house and hurried out to discover the explanation. There was a new male apparently bent on luring the lady Magnolia from her home. The wrathful husband chased the newcomer around and about, but the impudent stranger would pop up unabashed on top of a juniper bush, singing his song with as much assurance as if he expected an extra two syllables to captivate the lady. This contest continued for ten minutes or so, the warblers answering each other, each singing his own song consistently, until the interloper departed. At seven o'clock there was only *weechy weech* to be heard, and this appeared to have a triumphant ring; it was sung practically all morning long, as if the little warbler were guarding his home with redoubled zeal.

On July 6th at 8:15 in the morning the nest still contained eggs. I visited it again late in the day:

"The female is very loathe to leave. The nest contains the tiniest baby birds I have ever seen—three wee blind orange-red infants, naked except for a few tiny tufts of black down. While I watch a minute or two, they move about as if missing their mother's warmth."

The next morning at 9:52 I quietly settled myself in a chair fifteen feet north of the nest in the shade of a cedar and partly concealed by it. At 9:56 the mother appeared, seemed disturbed, flirted her tail, sat in the cedar south of the nest and uttered a gentle *tit*. At 10:03 she went to the young and brooded them without feeding. She left at 10:17, returned in three minutes, fed the babies quickly, waited a moment, and then flew away. When she came back, however, she was overcome with timidity, and stood about with an insect in her bill, flirting her tail and saying *tit, tit, tit*. Suddenly the male appeared with uplifted tail and quivering wings—evidently a courting attitude; she flew to a near-by cedar, he followed, and both disappeared. In a minute or two she came to the nest and started to brood; immediately her mate alighted on the brim, she slipped off and he followed.

The next day father began to realize the situation, for he fed seven times to his mate's thirteen in three hours of observation. Her colors were less bright than his, and her back grey where his was black. To avoid the sun I moved nearer and nearer to the nest, until at last I was only five feet from it, unconcealed in any way; yet the little birds accepted my presence without protest:

"It is a great triumph to be so near.

"Mother comes to the nest followed by a female Black-throated Green Warbler who stops on the juniper about 8 inches below her. Mother feeds the young with much 'chewing,' then deals with the visitor. Both fly, and I hear scufflings in the bushes."

Twice a red squirrel worried me by passing through the birches and cedars not far from the nest. I watched again from 6:00 to 7:00 P.M. and was treated to a veritable chorus of song, a Chewink and Maryland Yellowthroat singing almost in my ear and my warbler giving 242 songs.

Father now became more and more interested in his babies, and every day while I watched he brought more meals than did his mate. Indeed so wrapped up was he in paternal activities that he even forgot to sing! During twelve hours in four and a half days I recorded only fourteen songs.

On the afternoon of July 9th the squirrel came to a blueberry bush about five yards east of the nest and started to eat the unripe berries; I wrathfully arose and drove him away. The little mother must have been near, for when four minutes later she came with a caterpillar, she seemed timid all at once and could not screw up her courage to come to the north entrance which was so near to me. She shortly solved her problem by coming into the narrow east opening for the first time; she fed a baby and settled down to brood.

The next day I was disturbed to see that the squirrel was about again. A curious change had come over me during these days of watching the little brood; before this I had never felt any enmity towards red squirrels, and although I knew from my reading that they robbed birds' nests, I had never felt called upon to interfere. But now it was impossible for me to remain an impartial observer. My affection for these particular birds had grown so strong that my attitude had changed into one of fierce guardianship. I had read Henry Mousley's account of the "rascally squirrels" that had eaten his Black-throated Blue Warbler babies and of his regret that he had not shot them; I planned to profit from his sad experience. When I returned in the afternoon I was armed with a shotgun.

As I sat there waiting, six feet from the nest, the female seemed a little troubled. My proximity, added to the fact that

I was dressed in khaki instead of my usual green dress, seemed to tax her wits; she did not waste time objecting, but squeezed in between the juniper branches from the south—a brand-new way of entrance. At her next visit she came to the north entrance, but after that, four times in succession, she struggled in from the south, always leaving, however, by the large north door. As she was peacefully brooding after the last feeding, a rustle in the blueberry bush announced the arrival of the enemy; a few moments later that menace was ended and a great load had been lifted from my mind. But the poor little mother had darted away at the sound of the terrible report.

The next morning it was plain to be seen that I was eyed with great disfavor by the mother bird after yesterday's experience; she spent almost the whole hour that I watched, in chipping at me. She fed the young only three times and brooded once for two minutes. She was clearly much agitated; she did not hunt for food—except for herself—but sat and preened herself to an accompaniment of *tits* at the rate of about thirty a minute. One of her most used perches was in the cedar just behind me, which brought her much nearer to me than if she had been at the nest. I did not record each and every *tit,* but I calculated that in that short space of time I had been reproved with at least a thousand.

The morning of July 12th was windy, a circumstance that brought repeated disappointment to three baby birds, who mistook the motion caused by the wind for that made by their parents' arrival:

"The nest is rocked by a breeze; frantic head wavings.

"Another breeze; more frustrated hopes.

"A great jerk from the wind; two hopeful heads appear—no, three.

"The male is in the cedar with a spider, comes directly to

the nest, feeds and flies to the west, leaving two quivering excited mouths unsatisfied."

At this juncture the children could hardly be called handsome from our standpoint as they gaped over the edge of the nest with big red and yellow open bills, black goggle eyes tightly shut and tufts of black down standing pompadour.

The Male Magnolia Chases Away a Trespassing Myrtle Warbler

Although the foolish little female seemed to have forgiven me on the 12th, her agitation returned the next day:

"She devotes her whole mind to protesting against me. She gives 50 *tits* in one minute, coming within three feet of me. This grows a little wearisome. . . .

"She is still objecting about every other second in the cedar a few feet above me. I seem to have a horrid fascination for her."

Again the morning was windy, but the babies were wiser; no breeze could fool them now they were seven days old.

"Devoted daddy is back again; feeds two children. The darling little fellow comes searching for food within a few feet of me; gets two aphids for himself. Chases off a male Myrtle Warbler.

"A Chickadee looks like quite a giant to me now that I measure everything by the dainty proportions of my warblers.

"The female actually feeds, following her mate and crowding him aside. I suppose he gives her confidence."

On July 14 a great change had taken place, for the nestlings had been transformed overnight into bonny, fluffy, baby birds. Moreover, father was in full song again, giving *weechy weech* loud and strong. During the last three days I had missed this simple lay of his.

"Mother comes squeezing in through the prickly branches from the south. She feeds and then stands as if meditating upon the matter of brooding; at last settles down.

"The Red-eyed Vireo, Field Sparrow, Chewink, Yellowthroat, and Hermit Thrush all sing.

"Little mother looks very sweet on the nest, the picture of content with her soft blue-greys and her bright yellow breast.

"She moves a bit as if somewhat buffeted by hungry heads. She settles calmly down again with the air of knowing better than her children what is good for them."

Although father was singing so constantly, in three hours he fed the young eighteen times—twice as often as did his mate. So busy was he with both occupations that one minute's record stands thus:

"9:56. *Weechy weech.* Male in cedar with food, feeds, leaves. *Weechy weech.*"

Both songs were given as always while he was out of sight.

The nestlings were all the time growing more active; they stretched, rearranged themselves, preened their wings, and sometimes stood up on their feet. Once they nearly stepped out of the nest in their eagerness to welcome their father. For the first time I heard them give a note, a faint *zee, zee, zee.*

An hour in the afternoon of the 15th gave different results from any before; there was no singing and no brooding and only two meals brought, both by the male. The female came once with a caterpillar but must have eaten it herself; she spent thirty-eight of the sixty minutes in scolding. The curious thing was the wide variety of notes employed by her on this occasion, who before, with one small exception of five *eeps,* had confined herself to the wearisome iteration of *tit.* This time she began with *tits,* but all at once introduced a loud *yap* and again an *eep.* One series went like this: *eep, yeep, peep, tit, tit, yap, yeep*—the new notes being deeper and harsher than the old *tit.* Meanwhile the young kept very quiet. Father had come with food, but seemed to be impressed by his wife's perturbation, for he also ate his caterpillar and began to *tit* at me. She continued *pip, yip, yip, yap, eep.* Later father fed his children while mother indulged in her everlasting *tit.* The last notes I heard were *yeep, teep, tit, tit.*

Most unfortunately I was not able to visit the nest again until 8:30 the next morning, when to my bitter disappointment I found it empty. Although I searched and searched I never found the brood nor their mother, although father I often saw and heard singing until the end of July.

It had been a never-to-be-forgotten experience—these hours watching the exquisite little birds and listening to many bird songs, the loveliest of which was that of the Hermit Thrush. The Magnolia Warblers gave me my initiation into bird watching, and, although later I was to spend far more time at warbler nests, each of which possessed its particular fascination, yet none of them held quite the same enchantment for me as this little family nesting in the juniper.

CHAPTER 13

The Warblers in the Hemlocks

ONE of the prettiest songs in all the Grey Rocks woods is that of the Black-throated Green Warbler. He has a passion for singing, this little bird with the yellow cheeks, black throat, and greenish back, and his charming *trees, trees, murm'ring trees* seems to express the very spirit of a drowsy summer afternoon among the hemlocks.

Early one July morning a female Black-throated Green Warbler chipped at me as I was walking in the woods; my hopes rose; I followed her and soon discovered a small bunch on a hemlock branch some fifteen feet from the ground. I had found my warbler nest.

Returning after breakfast, I settled myself comfortably with pillows on the ground twenty feet from the nest; the accommodating little lady was intent on her eggs and troubled herself not at all about me. Her routine, both this day and the next, was to sit quietly for about three-quarters of an hour, then suddenly dart off and out of sight, not to return for ten to twenty minutes. Her more brightly colored mate came into sight but once, yet a large portion of the space in my notebook was concerned with him, for he sang incessantly from the hemlock grove to the east of the nest, usually about forty yards away, occasionally nearer, and again too far away to be distinctly heard.

On July 11, two days after the discovery of the nest, the babies hatched. Mother brooded them and brought them tiny

A Black-throated Green Warbler Family

insects, while father sang 1,445 songs in the seven hours I watched. Several times in the next few days mother gave vehement chips on the nest when her husband's singing drew near. If this was a signal for him to come and investigate, he failed to heed it. On and on he sang, ignorant of the fact that he was a father, oblivious of his duty as guardian. A Blackburnian Warbler sang close to the nest, a strange Black-throated Green male came to call, and also a Chickadee; these visitors had to be chased off by mother. I climbed the tree to admire the three babies, but father knew nothing of any danger to his household.

This never-ending singing inspired me with the idea of watching the family for a whole day and thereby establishing a record of songs from one bird in one day that would be truly astounding. My husband promised to help with the vigil, which was set for the 16th. Since the nest was a full half-mile from the house and in the midst of the woods, on the preceding afternoon I blazed a trail for the morning by sticking large pieces of paper on branches all along our usual route.

The stars were shining as I started out at 2:15, but the woods were pitchy black. It was an eerie experience in the darkness, my only light that cast by a feeble flashlight. Once I was lost and had to turn back to get my bearings. From one dim newspaper to the next I made my uncertain way, and it was with a sense of achievement that I at last reached my seat by the hemlock. All was darkness around me and there was no sound but the dripping of water off the leaves from a rain earlier in the night:

"3:12 (Eastern standard time). I can just begin to see the outlines of bushes around me.

"3:22. I can see quite a little now. One could find one's way home now without a flashlight.

"3:23. A bird note; a Scarlet Tanager sings to the south.

"3:25. The Tanager to the west answers.

"3:27. Both are singing constantly.

"3:41. A Hermit Thrush in the distance; Tanagers are still giving their proud songs. I cannot see colors yet; everything is a pale grey.

"3:52. THE WARBLER BEGINS! Thirty-three minutes

before sunrise. I have to use the flashlight to read my watch. I cannot yet see the nest.

"3:58. I can begin to see colors now and can read the watch without help of the light.

"4:08. The first *teacher* song from the Ovenbird to the west.

"4:14. MOTHER SUDDENLY DARTS OFF.

"4:17. The Tanagers have stopped at last after nearly an hour of constant singing.

"4:18. Mother returns with a green larva, *chips,* and feeds for 31 seconds. I could not see her very clearly at the nest."

Father in the meantime sang steadily at the rate of some seven to eight songs a minute until 4:20, when he stopped abruptly, perhaps for a bit of breakfast, but began again four minutes later, giving 379 songs the first hour.

At 6:57 my husband arrived to take over the watch, and I tramped home to breakfast. All day long one or the other of us watched, seeing little mother bring large meals at her customary leisurely pace from one to five times an hour, a total of forty-six meals in the sixteen hours.

As evening approached, the anthem of the Wood Thrush rang out, and the sweet music of the Wood Pewee was heard. Our Warbler and the Tanager sang a little past sunset, then fell silent. At 7:44 mother settled for the night, it then being so dark I could hardly see her.

What of our world's record, the motive which had induced us to undertake this all-day watching? By some perversity of fate that annoying little bird hardly sang at all, or, what is more likely, elected to sing so far away that we could not be sure whether it was he or a neighbor. To our chagrin we counted but 1,313 songs, whereas on July 14th his record had been 1,519 songs in six hours and the next day 1,680 in seven hours. A really typical day should have resulted in well over three thousand songs.

There was no chance to attempt another all-day record, for, much to my regret, I had to leave Pelham at noon on the 17th, entrusting the study of our little birds to my husband. The next day I began to worry that I had not warned him against examining the nest. I thought of telegraphing him, but in our family a telegram is sent only in emergencies, and as this seemed rather silly, I did nothing and hoped for the best.

The first word that greeted me on my return to Grey Rocks the afternoon of the 19th was, "The babies have left the nest." Hastening down in the woods, I met my regretful husband, who that morning had innocently climbed the tree, never dreaming that eight-day-old nestlings would be upset. To his dismay two jumped out; one he could not find, the other he put back twice, and for a few minutes it remained. Upon mother's return, however, out it went again. With her family thus dispersed, mother's tactics changed at once; instead of bringing food from a distance at long intervals, she gathered it in the vicinity and fed her scattered babies at short intervals. Three babies in three places stimulated her to tripled activity. During eleven hours on the 17th and 18th and early on the 19th, she had brought thirty-four meals, an average of 2.6 an hour; on the 19th after the dispersal of her family she administered sixty-three meals in eight hours, or 7.9 times an hour.

My husband's notes describe the busy scene:

"Baby 2 fluttering wings and hopping about in a small hemlock begging for food. Mother rushing about trying to find food, gently chipping.

"She ate a caterpillar herself; is searching within three feet of me.

"Objecting with bill full of caterpillars to Blue Jays near by.

"Had a fight with an Ovenbird. Ovenbird chased her."

All this excitement at last penetrated to the father of the family:

"11:44. Male is very near, much excited.

"11:50. Female chased him away; rushed at him twice.

"11:52. Baby 2 napping on limb near me.

"11:55. *Male has worm to feed!*

"11:59. Female feeds baby in the nest.

"12:00. Leave for Grey Rocks after four hours' observation."

The notes begin again at 1:13, but no more word of father warbler appears until 3:52, when he was seen hopping about with food in his bill:

"4:01. Male fed at last—a lovely sight!

"4:08. Male again fed the nest baby. Male and female chipping gently to each other. Female seemed pleased.

"4:40. Both birds at the nest at the same time. Female feeds, then male feeds, gently chipping."

At six o'clock I had finally reached my longed-for goal. Ten minutes later mother came and fed the nest baby, and after seven more minutes I first saw father at the nest. He had brought a tiny insect, staying at the nest a full minute and a half. Twice more he came, each time feeding the nest baby with care and deliberation, putting the morsels far down the little bird's throat, as if it were newly hatched. Mother, on the other hand, at this stage popped the food into the open bills very quickly, staying on the nest rim some twenty seconds.

This evening mother gave her last meal at 7:01, and then was seen no more. Father sang in the grove till 7:30, four minutes after official sunset, while the Tanager did not stop until 7:42. Baby 1 slept in a dogwood bush; Baby 2, in a low hemlock; and Baby 3 was all alone in the nest.

The next morning at 4:28 father was busily singing in his favorite grove, while mother was just as busily caring for her three children. Baby 1 had moved farther to the east and could no longer be watched. Baby 2 was trying to preen himself on his hemlock spray and nearly fell off.

At 5:45 father bethought himself of his family and appeared at the nest with a green caterpillar which he gave to his child. Baby 3 stretched and stretched, then rapidly flapped his wings. At 7:12 mother brought him a caterpillar, staying only five seconds. The next minute—

"*Baby steps out of the nest;* walks unsteadily along the branch to the west, nearly losing his balance every other moment. Settles down eight inches away and takes a first view of the great world. Says *chip*. He is very cunning, yellow and black and buffy with tufts of down here and there.

"Mother meantime is chipping at the other side of the hemlock. Suddenly she spreads herself completely and has a scuffle with a visiting Red-eyed Vireo. Red-eye disappears, and mother drops to the ground."

And now came a drama that I would not have believed had I not seen it with my own eyes. I had read in popular accounts of parent birds "urging their young to fly," but I had taken this with a grain of salt:

"Mother chips and chips; gets a small insect, comes to the baby, *hops over him,* comes back, all the time chipping, but leaves without feeding him. He is excited and tries to follow, but is so uncertain on his wobbly legs that he can hardly keep his balance and nearly falls three times. He then begins to preen his fluffy self."

Father then appeared for the first time since his youngest had left home:

"He comes to the nest with a larva, hops on the east rim, and then to the west rim, apparently at a loss what to do. Babe sits with bill wide open, expectant but silent. He then gives a *chip* or two; father goes to him and feeds him."

In the next hour and a quarter mother fed the baby four times. He cuddled down on the broad branch and took a nap.

Once more father appeared, this time with two little insects. These he tried again and again to *feed to the nest.* Baby called softly, father went to him and tried to feed him in the same manner, putting his bill in and out of baby's throat, but the latter was no longer used to taking food in this way. Mother came to a twig just below the baby and quivered her wings; father descended to her with his bill still full and gave her a small morsel. Back he went to the nest, she following; both stood on the rim, she quivered her wings. She picked the food out of his bill, went to Baby 3, but instead of giving it to him, took it to Baby 2 on the hemlock spray.

Both babies called vigorously before mother returned from an hour's vacation. At 10:24 she fed Baby 3, then three minutes later came with a larva but held it up out of reach, and flew six feet west on the branch. He hurried after her as best he could, while she came part way to meet him; when he reached her she retreated another foot, but at last rewarded him three feet from the nest. Father came to the nest, tried to feed his insect there, looked about for the baby, and went to him, but the little bird failed to open his mouth. This unresponsiveness may have disappointed father, for never again did I see this debonair gentleman troubling himself over his family.

"11:33. Mother chips and chips, baby answers; she comes into the home tree, gets a caterpillar, shows it to babe, then flies a little distance, constantly chipping. Babe starts out, making progress mostly by hops, but also by tiny flights. Has several tumbles and lands on a limb six feet below his starting point. Mother is near by with insect, chipping, but will not feed. Baby makes a great effort, and falls to the ground. Mother drops down beside him and flies north; baby starts after her in answer to her chipping. She keeps near him, usually above, chipping and dangling her worm. At last she feeds him. Gets another worm at once, and the same play is reenacted.

"He is now more expert in making progress. He climbs into a little pine fifty feet from the starting point and rests."

In the afternoon we caught Baby 3 to band him; he squealed, and mother appeared and dashed about near us with her tail drooped and spread, and her wings held straight up. We released the baby, and mother joined him and mounted little bushes as if showing him what to do. We saw mother and her babies the next two days, but after that they wandered deeper into the woods.

In the majority of cases noted by other observers and by myself, the male Black-throated Green Warbler has helped care for his children. This particular male was probably young and inexperienced; and furthermore there had been an evident lack of cooperation between him and his wife in the matter of the location of the nest, which was so far away from his favorite singing stations that he remained unaware of happenings at the nest—the presence of enemies or even the existence of his own offspring.

CHAPTER 14

On Watching an Ovenbird's Nest

ONE Monday in July as I wandered through the woods, I was suddenly stopped by loud protestations. Looking about, I saw an Ovenbird on a branch with his bill full of grubs while below on the ground beside the Dutch oven of a nest stood the mother bird, staring up at me absolutely motionless. As I walked towards her, she flew up, adding her objections to those of her mate. Inside the nest were two tiny infants, blind and naked. I retired behind a bush twenty feet away, effacing myself as much as possible, but the commotion kept on unabated. All the neighbors came to sympathize or look on—another pair of Ovenbirds, a Black and White Warbler, a Chestnut-sided Warbler, a Black-throated Green Warbler, a Phoebe, and a Chewink.

After a while father with a moth in his bill descended to the ground, flew up again, scolded and scolded, raising his orange crown and jerking his tail; then flew down again and ran towards the nest still objecting. His mate became frantic with alarm, on seeing such rash conduct; he reconsidered, flew up above the nest, ate his insect, and devoted himself to reproaches.

Seeing that the situation was hopeless, I moved forty feet away across the brook, seating myself beside a rock and behind a small hop hornbeam tree; with my glasses I could see the happenings at the nest. At once there was peace, and in two minutes mother went to the young to brood them. Soon Father came with a big spider and caterpillar; his mate slipped out and waited while he fed the babies, returning to them when he left.

Mother brooded and brooded, then slipped quietly off and walked away. For a long time she stayed away, finally reappearing as stealthily as she had left, bringing with her a large meal. The most striking thing about the routine of an Ovenbird's household is its deliberateness—broodings three-quarters of an hour long, meals sometimes an hour and a half apart—all in marked contrast to the ways of most warblers, whose broodings are short, and who bring food every five to ten minutes.

It seemed as if life stood still for me while I devoted myself to this nest, as if I had endless leisure to look, to enjoy, to think, alone in this pleasant place in the woods. The stately clusters of evergreen wood fern, the sun-dappled water beeches and hemlocks, the tiny waterfall—to these I could give but fleeting glances, for always I had to concentrate on the rocks and brown leaves about the center of activities of mother Ovenbird. A baby tree bowed; I seized my glasses, for any movement in that region was fraught with possible meaning. But the alarm was false. It is curious how one small branch will bend with a breeze that nothing else feels. In these vigils I learned much of the ways of the wind.

Often there was no sound but that of the tumbling brook. Sometimes there were discordant notes. A soft pattering across the leaves, and suddenly a red squirrel vented his wrath at my presence by the strangest of squeaks and squeals, more like those we expect from a toy than those from a real animal. A grey squirrel flirted his handsome tail in quirks and curlicues and then exploded into a snarling, jarring string of vituperations, extraordinary noises to proceed from such a soft and furry little beast.

The birds were pure delight. The Scarlet Tanager threw a wild, proud challenge to the woods in keeping with his gorgeous plumage. The solemn, continuous strain of the Red-

The Ovenbird's Rustic Bower

eyed Vireo embodied the very spirit of serenity and content. Most beautiful of all was the song of the Hermit Thrush; when heard near by it has a note of courage, of triumph over the difficulties of life; at a distance it expresses ineffable sweetness and peace.

Mother Ovenbird had her notions; she did not mind me looking at her when she was by the nest, but if ever I caught sight of her on her way there, she froze at once, and would not be reassured until I had put down the offending glasses.

It was curious that on Tuesday morning, of the five intervals between the meals she brought, four lasted exactly forty-eight minutes each.

That afternoon I noted:

"How pretty mother looks inside her rustic bower! She steps out and views the weather, which is threatening; then withdraws again to shelter."

Father was an almost negligible factor in the home life during the first half of the week, for he seldom came with food, sometimes absenting himself for an afternoon at a time, and he did not even proclaim his territory with the loud, insistent *teacher teacher teacher teacher,* as is the custom of his kind earlier in the season. On Wednesday I was shocked to see a Hermit Thrush chase him three times, when he had had one of his rare impulses to bring food to the young.

Although most of the authorities state that male and female Ovenbirds are identical in appearance, I was glad to find that I could distinguish my birds, not only by the brighter orange crown of the male, but particularly by the color of their backs, father's being more golden brown, and mother's having more of an olive cast.

Mr. Mousley "never once approached the nest" of the Ovenbirds he was studying; but by choosing my time I could steal across the brook each day and admire the progress of the babies without the parents being any the wiser. Although little Ovenbirds are fed so seldom in comparison with most other baby birds, their meals make up in size what they lack in number. I was repeatedly astonished at the enormous mouthfuls of spiders, caterpillars and moths that were brought to the young.

Thursday afternoon there came a change in the schedule. Mother gave up brooding and guarded instead, mounting a near-by bush and sitting quietly for fifteen minutes or so, her handsome black-streaked breast puffed out—a picture of motherly satisfaction. Father suddenly woke up to his responsibilities, and for the rest of the week outdid his mate in bringing food. Instead of meals appearing once every forty-two minutes, they now came at the rate of once in twenty minutes, the difference being largely due to father's zeal, since mother kept on the even tenor of her way, hardly hastening her return at all.

On Saturday morning the young had been fed at 10:35 and I was beginning to feel that it was full time they received further attention:

"11:35. A bird flies down two yards from the nest. She feeds; then the male comes walking over the leaves. She steps aside for him while he feeds. Strangely enough a gaping, reproachful mouth waves at them as they leave, like a comic picture of a ferocious snake. Did both large portions go into one maw?"

On Sunday morning as I neared the familiar spot, I heard mother scolding very hard and fast. It was plain that something had happened; I went directly to the nest and found it empty. I had never dreamt that the precocious little creatures would leave so soon. How could they have deserted their warm, dry, cozy home for the wild wet woods?

Sadly I returned to my accustomed post; soon it was evident that one baby was near the nest in mother's charge, while the other was in a bed of ferns tended by father. So I watched the family for some time, not realizing how far a little Ovenbird may travel at such a tender age; when I went to investigate, mother's babe was far away and well hidden. The fern bed was a baffling place to search, but all at once I heard a shrill *peep peep peep;* following the sound I discovered baby looking like a little light brown leaf, the fuzz of down outside his feathers giving him a very odd appearance.

His tail had barely sprouted, and his flight feathers were not unsheathed; he could not possibly have flown, but his legs were strong and well developed.

I gently picked him up and he was not a bit afraid; in a few minutes he went to sleep in my hand. Father appeared with a caterpillar, but instead of going through the extravagant demonstration of alarm I expected, merely gave a loud *tchip* and vanished. Baby began to preen himself, then said *peep* and again *peep*. A mosquito started to bite my hand, and I brought it in front of the little bird as a small tidbit; but he did not peck at it till it flew. Another alighted on his wing and sucked itself full, while I perceived a new bond of sympathy between birds and people.

Presently baby grew hungry and called more and more frequently, so I returned him to his twig and went back to my hornbeam. Louder and more persistent came his far-reaching cries, until I could not help thinking how easily an enemy might find him. It was time for me to go home; as I passed the fern bed I stepped on a dead twig that snapped—instantly there was silence. I do not suppose the little fellow had ever heard this sound before, but something in his inherited make-up told him it spelled danger. I was not able to visit this family again, but I hope they escaped the perils of youth, and journeyed South in safety.

By good fortune the next summer I again discovered an Ovenbird's nest in the Grey Rocks woods in mid-July. The mother flew quietly away from her three eggs, but the following day she behaved differently. While her mate scolded at my approach, she hurried off, then turned back, and ran about in a peculiar attitude with her back hunched, wings dragging, tail spread fanwise and body feathers puffed out. There was no simulation of injury, but she certainly did look strange and conspicuous and well suited to draw the attention of an unsophisticated enemy to herself.

The next morning (which happened to be Monday) two babies had hatched. I settled myself twenty feet away behind a little hemlock, thankful that neither parent had seen me look at their progeny. Before long there was a rustle in the great hemlock to the south and I became motionless while mosquitoes settled over my face. I felt like St. Macarius who, inadvertently crushing a gnat and thereby missing an opportunity of enduring mortification patiently, stationed himself for six months in the marshes of Scete. Fortunately for me, little mother took only three minutes to decide that I was not too alarming a neighbor. She flew to the ground and walked to the nest where she fed the babies and stepped in to brood. Then I began once more on my occupation of reducing the pests of the world.

Mother hovered her children for fifty-four minutes, then walked away, but to my surprise returned in ten minutes with another large meal—the other mother had never spent less than seventeen minutes away. This time she waited in the hemlock two minutes and the next time only one, and after that bothered no more about me. How my heart warmed to her for her good sense and devotion!

Her mate, unfortunately, felt differently about me. He came once that morning to bestow a morsel on his offspring, but upon spying me, he started to scold and for one half-hour he protested; then he departed, not to be seen again that day nor the next. In an attempt to calm his nerves, I moved farther away; but even that concession did not reassure him. Sometimes I heard his loud announcement of ownership and very occasionally the ecstatic flight song; but he refused to risk his precious skin by coming near me.

For three days the routine varied very little; long broodings; sometimes long, sometimes short, absences from the nest; ten large meals brought during eight hours the first day, eleven the next, and fourteen the next—and every bit of the work done by mother. Oddly enough there were two intervals of forty-eight minutes on this Tuesday, one of forty-six, and one of forty-four.

Wednesday father appeared with a contribution; but instead of feeding his babies all he did was to reprove me, raise his crest, flutter his wings, and give a curious, soft, three-syllabled note to his mate. She, as if in a spirit of bravado to show him the unreasonableness of his fears, did a thing without precedent, for she dropped directly down to the nest from a branch above it. (Every other time she walked from quite a distance to the nest.) Still he remained stubbornly distrustful.

One day I had a philosophic thought; namely, that pleasure was given to three sets of beings by the occasional visits from the biting flies: First, it must seem like a banquet to the flies to discover me still and tasty in the woods. Next, there was a distinct feeling of achievement within me when I dispatched the creatures. And finally the carcass was a boon to the ant that carried it off for a dinner with her sisters. My philosophizings vanished, however, the next day when I was attacked by an army of deer flies. I used to think the etymology of Beelzebub—"king of the flies"—was a prophetic reference to the noxious germs given us by our satellite the housefly, but now I knew better; it was these little demons that were meant.

This year as last, Thursday afternoon showed a change in the home life; but this time the male had no part in it. First, mother gave up brooding; then, instead of walking directly away when leaving the nest as heretofore, she browsed around for a few minutes in front of the nest, finding small insects for herself; twice she flew away instead of leaving on foot; and finally she fed her three children twice as often as before.

The first three and one-half days she had brought meals once in forty minutes on an average; this afternoon she presented them once every nineteen minutes. I looked forward eagerly to what the next day would bring forth, in further variations in her behavior and a possible reform on the part of her mate.

As I watched little mother, I longed to know more of her life. I wished I could have seen the courtship, could have viewed the construction of the quaint little home, and then could have followed the fortunes of the young family after their first venture into the world, and somehow could have known how they found their way on the incredible journeys to South America and back to these Massachusetts woods. A great admiration for this quiet little bird arose in me, for her self-sufficiency, the simplicity of her life unencumbered by the possessions that overwhelm us human beings. Here she was her own architect, her own provider, bringing up her babies independently of doctors, nurses, books, and even her husband, facing unaided the elements and prowling enemies.

Each evening I left a blessing with the brave little bird, and each morning was happy to find all well. But Friday as I walked through the woods, I noticed that big mushrooms that had been standing for several days were now lying low, gnawed by some animal. A sense of foreboding caused me to go straight to the nest as soon as I reached my hemlock; the home was empty and beside it lay five feathers from little mother's wing. I trust the gallant little bird had escaped with her life.

CHAPTER 15

Misadventures of a Pair of Bell Vireos

IN THICKETS of sand plums, patches of young willows, or shrubbery in gardens, lives a small olive-green and yellowish bird that is seldom seen but often heard. Plainly clad, and endowed with only a funny little song, nevertheless the Bell Vireo is one of my favorites among Oklahoma birds. All day long and all summer long he gives his *jiggledy jiggledy jiggledy jig,* sometimes as often as twelve or sixteen times a minute, after which he rests a bit. There is no music to this refrain, but there is a quaint charm in its enthusiasm, in the rapid jumble of it all.

One of the best spots for bird study on the campus of the University of Oklahoma used to be the garden around the greenhouse, where many ornamental trees and shrubs had been planted. It was here on May 12, 1926, that I heard ecstatic singing from a Bell Vireo in a honeysuckle bush; I stooped and discovered an exquisite little nest hanging only fifteen inches above the ground; in it was one egg. The birds had made the most of their opportunities in materials, for bark from an exotic birch near by was the mainstay of the structure, which was covered on the outside with spider webs, cocoons, and bark fibers, and lined with horsehair and fine pieces of peppergrass stems.

Three more eggs were laid, and on the 28th there were three tiny babies in the nest, the next morning four.

I put my campstool in a shady spot twenty-five feet from the nest and waited. Mother returned to brood, while father busied himself bringing food and singing; but he did not like my field glasses. The next day I moved to a position only fifteen feet away; here without my glasses the birds minded me far less than when I had been farther away but had used them.

Male and female warblers usually differ in their plumages; the Song Sparrows that I studied in later years were distinguished by bright-colored bands, but the Bell Vireos wore no bands and looked exactly alike. Fortunately one usually proclaimed his identity with *jiggledy jiggledy jig;* he had also been more disturbed by the bird glasses than his mate had been. Later, however, when, driven by the sun, I moved within ten and even eight feet of the nest, he accepted me as harmless, while she raised objections. She did not seem to be afraid, for she came to the nest without nervousness and cared for her children, but she voiced her displeasure while brooding the young.

On approaching the nest, the parents alighted in the top of the honeysuckle and descended by easy stages, their soft colors blending with the lights and shadows on the leaves. As I watched them I noted the songs of their neighbors, Mourning Dove and Lark Sparrow, Baltimore and Orchard Oriole, Yellow Warbler and Bewick Wren, Wood Pewee and Mockingbird.

Although mother did most of the brooding, father occasionally took a turn. On June 1st he settled down on the nest, ruffled up and scolding; but mother appeared promptly, and he slipped off.

The next day she was much annoyed when she saw me:

"7:47. She comes to the nest with a green caterpillar; is so indignant at me that she flirts her tail and scolds energetically. She hops away and swallows her insect; scolds some more with crest raised.

"7:49. Both come to the nest at the same time; she feeds the young. He gives his food to her; *she eats it herself and flies away*. I call this greedy."

The 3rd of June was cool, and the male sang three times as much as on the previous days, all of which had been hot:

"9:18. Father gives a song in the home bush; feeds, then inspects for two minutes. Pops down to brood.

"9:21. Mother in bush; he leaves as she comes to the nest. She scolds, feeds, scolds, broods, scolds.

"9:22. Scolds and scolds and scolds. He is singing to the north.

"9:24. She is now brooding quietly.

"9:25. A song in the bush, another; father descends with a caterpillar and gives it to his wife. She scolds and scolds and scolds, holding the worm in her bill.

"9:28. He sings nine times a minute.

"9:29. She is still scolding with the worm in her bill. The flies are biting me viciously and she disapproves of my retaliations.

"9:31. He comes with a big insect, but her bill is already full. He runs his creature along her bill, but in vain, for she remains motionless. With some difficulty he rearranges the object in his bill, swallows it himself, and flies away. She rises, gives the worm to a child, inspects, settles down, and once more takes up her scolding."

At 9:50 mother suddenly left; father came and after feeding hopped on to brood, but hurried away seven minutes later on the return of his mate. Back he came singing, with a great moth in his beak. It was surprising how well he could sing with such a mouthful.

In the periods of observation during the first five days of nest life, the male carried nearly three times as many meals to the nest as did his mate, the average rate at which food was brought being once every five minutes. Unlike the other birds I have studied, the female did not leave at her mate's approach, but took the food herself, and often ate it herself, a quite uncalled-for procedure in my eyes. Most birds are silent near the nest, but a Bell Vireo simply cannot repress his overflowing spirits.

On June 4th we had to leave Norman for the Wild Life Conference at the Wichita National Forest; and we did not return until the afternoon of the 8th. I hurried to look at my little family. The nest had been torn out—evidently the work of a cat.

A new nest, again largely made of birch bark, was located seventy-five yards to the east in a hydrangea bush. It looked as if the birds might have learned a lesson, for this nest was three feet above the ground. The day that I found it the male was singing a great deal in the home bush and a little in another bush near by. Once he dashed back to the hydrangea to drive away a Brown Thrasher—a David attacking Goliath. I heard a scuffling, but could not see just what happened.

The four tiny eggs, white with a few speckles, were laid from June 11th to the 14th. On the 22nd I had a charming experience with the pair. A parent left at my arrival; but four minutes later I heard scolding and the male gave four songs in the home bush. The next minute (9:37) a bird came to the nest, inspected and started to incubate.

"9:42. Parent is wiggling around a good deal.

"9:51. *He sings on the nest!*

"9:57. Sings again on the nest; moves about a great deal."

His enthusiasm gradually increased, and from one song a minute he was soon giving three, and finally as many as six. Apparently he was so happy that he just couldn't keep quiet.

Bell Vireos Building

After forty-one minutes on the nest, his mate approached. He sang to greet her and slipped off, then sang again. She gave a scold and settled on the nest.

Three days later I found that the cat, besides emptying the neighboring dove nests, had torn the bottom out of this little home.

The foolish little birds then returned to their first bush and started their third nest three feet from the ground. The male was in the highest of spirits, singing far more than during any other hour of observation, for he gave 125 songs in the home bush and 129 elsewhere. He also had a new note, something between the song and the scold—*spee spee*—with which he greeted his mate. The female was the chief architect; she made seven trips, but only twice could I see material in her bill. The male came sixteen times, as if he had to be always examining the structure, but I never saw anything in his bill, although I have seen other male Bell Vireos carrying material. As formerly in the brooding and incubating, he acted as if his mate had prior right to the nest and always hurried away when she came. I could not be sure whether he was helping or hindering, but he certainly was vastly interested in the enterprise and was always coming to tinker with it.

Most of the work on the nest was apparently done that day or early in the morning of the next, for at nine o'clock on June 27th it was practically all there, although not shaped at the bottom. Enthusiasm was decidedly less today, for each bird made but four trips in the hour I watched and the male sang only 99 times. Once the female brought a long piece of birch bark. Twice they came together, the female entering the nest and shaping it by turning around and around. The next time the male arrived alone and started to work with the fibers, teasing and stretching them, getting down into the nest and working most busily, in the meantime singing. His mate arrived above him and waited a moment until he noticed her, when he hurried off, saying *spee spee*.

On July 2nd I found the male admiring the first egg. Three days later the third disaster had taken place; the nest was upside down on the ground with two tiny white eggs and a large Cowbird's egg near by.

They did not try again. For a few days they remained in their territory, but after that the exuberant song was heard no more. The cat had done its work.

CHAPTER 16

Four Pet Mourning Doves

ONE afternoon in early September I boosted four-year-old Barbara up to a dove nest as the mother flew off and flapped hither and thither on the ground.

"What is in the nest?" I asked.

"One egg and one vat."

"What?"

"One egg and one mouse."

"*What* do you see?"

"One egg and one baby bird."

The naked red object in the nest had looked to the child more like a large newborn mouse than anything else she had ever seen; it was only my astonishment that made her conclude it must be something else.

About this time a friend of ours had come into possession of a young Mourning Dove that had been attacked by Blue Jays and a dog; she nursed him back to health and gave him to us. He was the tamest, gentlest, most polite of birds:

"Baby starts to pat him gently, but he tries to eat from her hand, pecking her a little; consequently she sets up a wail and turns for comfort to the quiet pet frog. Our visitor settles down and goes to sleep.

"Constance puts two hopping toads into his cage. He holds his wings straight up in the air in astonishment or fright, or perhaps to intimidate them."

Since one dove was so charming, we thought it would be pleasant both for him and for us to have another. So we visited one of the many nests we knew of on the campus of the University of Oklahoma and took a bird about nine days old. Our dove again lifted his wings to their highest extent, after which he ignored the newcomer. The children decided to call the birds Flower and Daisy. Soon I heard sweet little begging notes, and there was Daisy pursuing Flower, shaking his wings and asking to be fed; unkind Flower responded with pecks.

Daisy did not enjoy my method of stuffing bread and milk down his throat. He ran his bill frantically about my fingers, squealing and peeping and flapping his wings, but only occasionally opening his bill. He was searching for his parent's throat from which pigeon "milk" had been pumped into his beak. It took him five days to learn to drink out of the dish, seven to pick up weed seeds, and eleven to feed himself bread and milk—an accomplishment I hailed with relief.

As long as he could not feed himself, Daisy was tame, but just as he was getting to the point of independence, he began to strike at me with his wings when I fed him, and soon afterwards he became thoroughly timid and remained so ever after in marked contrast to Flower's friendliness.

Flower's affections were set on people; he preened our fingers, rode on our hands, and even accompanied family expeditions perched on the baby carriage. Although the most amiable of creatures with us, he was just the opposite with foolish little Daisy, who could not resist begging from an older bird of his own species despite the cruel treatment he received. When exasperated Flower grabbed him by the scalp, he did not try to escape, but patiently endured his punishment.

One day when Daisy must have been four weeks old, we took Flower into the living room, returning him an hour later to the table in the Dove Room. Daisy met him with terrific squeals and wing flappings, even sticking his bill into Flower's face in his joy at greeting what he took to be a long-lost parent. I did not wonder that Flower lost patience with such silly behavior and tweaked out Daisy's head feathers until that place was quite bare. Daisy could eat as well as Flower by this time.

Daisy soon gave up the begging and Flower the pecking, and the two became friends. The last of December I was amused to see that the tables had been turned. Both birds were hungry and hurried to the small box of seeds and grain I gave them. Flower pecked Daisy, but the latter returned this treatment with interest and drove the former tyrant out, eating most of the sunflower seeds himself. Back came Flower, driving Daisy away; Daisy promptly returned and chased Flower off. Flower retaliated, even pulling a feather out of his companion; but in the end Daisy was triumphant, and Flower retired to pick seeds off the floor.

In the winter the birds were moved out onto the sleeping porch; friendly Flower used to come through the window into one of the bedrooms to visit a member of the family convalescing from the flu, and Daisy would follow. I screened the window to Flower's disappointment; seeing little of people, he grew less tame, while Daisy became wilder than ever.

By February, Flower's neck was beautiful with ruby and purple iridescence, so we believed him to be a male, and this surmise was confirmed when we heard an imperfect coo on the 9th of this month. Daisy had so little iridescence that we hoped "he" might prove to be a female, but this was not the case.

"March 12. There is no hope now; both are males. This morning just as it became light I saw Flower cooing; I got him and weighed him in the south room and left him there for a while. Soon Daisy came down from his perch and *cooed* three or four times; he was apparently much disturbed at Flower's disappearance."

A month later I noted:

"They perch and sleep near each other and seem the best of friends. Lately Flower has been caressing Daisy, preening him, as if trying to make a mate out of him. Daisy usually hurries away, but once I saw them in a corner together where Daisy could not escape, and he was submitting with very good grace."

On April 15th Daisy was feeling droopy and I was shocked to see Flower pursuing him and pecking him; I had to shut him up awhile to reform him. I saw no more pecks, but the birds kept the length of the sleeping porch between them. Flower's behavior seemed particularly uncalled for, since two weeks earlier when *he* was feeling sick, Daisy had not persecuted him.

A few days later we banded the birds and took them out of doors. Flower sat contentedly on Constance's shoulder for about a minute; then the whistling of wings of a wild Mourning Dove was heard. Off whirled Flower like a cannon ball, and he and the wild dove disappeared from sight, followed by Daisy. Daisy never reappeared; Flower returned that afternoon and again the next day, but never afterwards.

Some years later we again tried to raise young doves with the hope that they might nest in the spring. The nucleus of our flock was a full-grown bird with an injured wing, caught on September 12th. The next day we added three others, about twelve to fourteen days old and ready to leave the nest. It was a happy family this time; the younger birds never flapped their wings and whimpered for food as Daisy had done (perhaps because they were older when taken from home than he had been); and the older bird never pecked them. All were tame, but none was a real pet as Flower had been. None of our doves showed curiosity or explored their environment in the amusing way that a Bobwhite which I once had for a pet had done.

In December we moved the birds into a fairly large outdoor cage ten feet from the sleeping porch. One night the door was not securely fastened, and a cat killed the oldest dove and one of the younger birds. Would the two survivors prove to be a pair or not?

In 1919 we had had two males; this year we began to fear we had two females. But on March 18th we changed our minds:

"An utter surprise. L is a male and coos—badly to be sure, but still I think it must be his first attempt at the regular song. At 1:45 he is 'charging' R. He stops every few minutes, puffs up his throat feathers, and gives a queer laborious coo of four notes, then after R he goes again. She (?) gives him a few pecks.

"March 23. L is cooing and trying to caress R, who pays no attention. L then runs along the perch looking up, as if, poor thing, he wanted to perform a nuptial flight.

"March 28. I see them preening each other's heads rapidly and affectionately. Maybe R is a lady after all."

Now that we apparently had a pair at last, we thought that they deserved fancier names than merely L and R, which referred to the left and right legs on which they were respectively banded. We decided upon Lionel and Artemis.

On the afternoon of April 3rd we fixed a nesting box in the cage and strewed dead grass and twigs on the floor. The next morning early Lionel was in the box giving the nest-call *coo-roo* in the proper attitude with head down, tail up, and wings flipping. Artemis soon settled herself in the box beside him and gave a similar note. The activities of the day were nest-calling, caressing each other, and fiddling with nesting material. Lionel would fly to the floor, search about, pick up twigs, and drop them again:

"9:30. The first twig has been brought to the nest, but it falls to the ground.

"10:28. Artemis is on the nest facing east; Lionel is beside her with a twig that drops to the floor. Now he gets a piece of grass; steps on her back, facing her tail, turns about, but drops the grass overboard. Returns with another piece, drops it *on her back!*"

Artemis perhaps grew discouraged, for she went to the floor and came back with a bunch of grass in her bill, placing it in a corner of the box. Lionel went into the box, picked up the grass, put it down, picked it up again, and flew to the floor with it and dropped it!

On April 6th the birds had mastered the building routine, Artemis staying in the nest, while Lionel brought material, stepped on her back and laid it down in front of her for her to arrange. At times he would try to make high flights, and she would give the nest-call, as if inviting him to bring her supplies.

The next day, however, the silly male busied himself carrying material *away* as well as to the nest.

On the 8th I wrote:

"They spend all morning apparently at nest-building, but the results are meager enough. At 1:30 I see something unusual: both are on the ground, Lionel flies to the nest and gives the nest-call; Artemis stays down searching about, gets a large twig, and flies up with it. She does not step on her husband's back, but gets in beside him and he leaves; she settles down and he goes to searching, but flies to the perch with an empty bill."

Late in the afternoon of the 10th Artemis laid her first egg. Although the parents had been working for a week, the box contained only a pitiful supply of material.

Two White Eggs

The next day I noted:

"The birds are busy sometimes on the nest and sometimes off; often the egg is pushed into a corner. Artemis has a little more idea of her duties than Lionel. I fear he needs some lessons in the responsibilities of young fathers."

On April 12th the second egg was laid, but the next morning I found a sad state of affairs:

"All the nesting material is out of the box! The two poor eggs are over in one corner."

Lionel was intent on starting over again; he gave seventy

nest-calls in twelve minutes. Since the eggs were ignored, I removed them.

On the afternoon of April 18th I noted:

"4:45. Lionel seems to be really bringing material in earnest, stepping on Artemis's back each time. No, I don't believe I should have said in earnest, *as he carries away about as much as he brings.*

"6:00. Artemis has an egg and not a scrap of material in the box! Constance fixes her an ample nest, which seems quite to trouble the poor lady. Finally she settles down and both spend the night on it."

The next day Artemis incubated fitfully during the day, when by all rights Lionel should have been on. By 3:10 every speck of their fine nest had disappeared! The next day Lionel managed to knock the eggs onto the floor.

"April 21. Silly Lionel nest-calls to some extent, but Artemis has lost enthusiasm; she sits indifferently on the perch. Later they caress each other affectionately."

The same story was repeated again and again. Lionel had a passion for nest-calling; his one idea was to start the nesting cycle over and over again as rapidly as possible, keeping his poor mate continually laying, the first egg of a new set appearing six days after the second egg of the last set. Not only did he fail to incubate in the daytime as he should, he would not leave his wife in peace when she tried to care for the eggs:

"May 17. Lionel is charging Artemis on the floor. Later he pecks her cruelly whenever she tries to sit on the eggs (her fifth set). By evening her head is bare in many places."

The next two times she laid but one egg, then two eggs, and again one egg. In sixty-nine days she had laid nine sets totaling fifteen eggs.

Finally, seeing that Lionel was incurably addlepated, we

released the birds, trusting that long-suffering Artemis would find herself a sensible husband.

Our experiences with pet Mourning Doves had been instructive, if not strikingly successful. Other people report captive birds of this species breeding normally and persistently. One family in Colorado, as related by Dr. Bergtold, found a dove an entertaining and intelligent pet, but this bird had no association with others of his kind after babyhood.

It is a happy thing that this beautiful bird has been able to adapt itself to civilization, that it is so widely distributed over the country, and that in many places its numbers are increasing. Dr. Wallace Craig gives a fine tribute to the touching song of our "turtledove":

"This strain impresses me as most beautifully melodious, not only when contrasted with bird songs of a far inferior order, but even in the pigeonry where the Zenaidura competes with the gentle cooers of the whole world. Some pigeons have more elaborate songs, but for romantic sweetness there is no pigeon song I ever heard which can approach that of our Mourning Dove."

CHAPTER 17

Herons with Golden Crowns

TO SOME people, the Olivers' woods near the Canadian River a mile and a half south of Norman might seem a gloomy, forbidding place with little but the great grey trees, the muddy water and fallen tree trunks; but to me it was a place of enchantment. Here East met West, for in this very piece of woods only two hundred yards apart nested a pair of Red-shouldered and a pair of Swainson Hawks—our most westerly record in Oklahoma for the first species and our most easterly for the second. Here is the only place in the county where we ever found Pileated Woodpeckers—unhappily only in the winter—and where we ever found the Acadian Flycatcher and Prothonotary and Sycamore Warblers summering. Near by a pair of Barred Owls raised four young.

The most abundant nesting birds in the particular fifteen acres of primeval trees were Red-bellied and Downy Woodpeckers, Crested Flycatchers, Wood Pewees, Cardinals, Red-eyed Vireos, Tufted Titmice, Plumbeous Chickadees, and Blue-grey Gnatcatchers. But it was the Yellow-crowned Night Herons that were the most fascinating to me, both because of their curious ways and because almost nothing seemed to be known of their home life.

In 1926 two pairs of these handsome birds had nested in neighboring trees in these woods where wild life is carefully protected by the enlightened owners. One nest was forty feet from the ground in a green ash; the other, thirty feet up in an elm.

The next spring, on April 10th a pair were in possession of the upper nest. Five days later, seated on a great log fifty yards distant, I watched the nest for an hour. Male and female in this species look alike, grey with white cheeks, golden crowns, and white plumes hanging down their backs. I assumed that the bird that spent the night on the nest was the female, and this seemed to be borne out by later events.

At 7:00 A.M. mother was incubating and father was standing a few feet above her. Suddenly he stuck his bill straight up in the air, crouched down with all his plumes erected, and uttered a loud *whoop,* immediately afterwards returning to standard heron attitude. This song and dance were repeated nine times, taking place about once a minute; the bird went through it quickly, nearly overbalancing himself as he made the very low bow. Then he started slowly and majestically towards his mate, who, at first unmoved by the performance, now began to watch him alertly. As he neared her he gradually raised his crest and wing coverts, looking amazingly different from the slim, sleek bird usually seen. His mate responded in like manner, then stepped off the nest abruptly and flew down to a fallen tree trunk. He entered the nest deliberately, turned over the eggs, and sat down to brood. Nine minutes after her departure his mate returned. Both birds displayed to each other; he left, and she took her place once more upon the nest.

On the 18th, I again watched from seven to eight in the

morning; but very little happened. One bird was incubating on the upper nest and its mate was not present. Two herons stood on the lower nest, and I thought that I should see some courting, but here again I was disappointed. Occasionally one lifted its plumes a little and ran its bill along the neck and side of the other, which reciprocated in like manner. Each preened itself, scratched itself, and yawned, but for the most part they stood perfectly motionless. Both flew away at half past seven; and I did not see them again, the lower nest remaining untenanted this season. Life was so deliberate at these herons' nests that every yawn was important, every scratch an event.

Unfortunately, these woods were not quite a paradise; in late April and early May the mosquitoes became so ferocious and so overwhelming in numbers, that whenever I visited the spot I hastened through it as fast as I could.

It was not until May 19th that I again watched the herons. My alarm clock for early morning trips had been the Purple Martins that burst out in song shortly before dawn. This morning, however, they first roused me at three; when they chattered again at four I thought it must be time to go. But when I had parked the car by the little farmhouse and climbed through the fence into the cotton field above my woods, I found it was still night—a cloudy night with a great warning wind that seemed to ask why I was not home in bed. At the edge of the woods deep blackness met me; I dared not venture through the tangle of trees and shrubs with no glimmer of light to help me pick my way down the steep bluff. So I skirted the fringe of woods until I came to a place with an open field below instead of forest, and here there was light enough to enable me to clamber down.

I was glad I had my faithful old revolver that had accompanied me on my solitary trips on horseback or on foot since

Yellow-crowned Night Heron

college days. What I would have shot, I am sure I do not know. It was a comfort, nevertheless, just as it had been many times before, in spite of the fact that I never had had occasion even to show it to an enemy.

When I reached my heron outpost, I could not see the birds at all; on going nearer I could barely discern the dim outline of mother standing on her nest. In fifteen minutes I could see the colors of things, and the woods began to look friendly instead of menacing. The bleak wind had its advantages, for it kept the mosquitoes at home. Very little happened at the heron nest for over an hour. Mother sometimes brooded and again stood up; she occasionally preened her feathers, and once or twice billed the babies. I grew weary of standing against a tree and wondered why father failed to appear; possibly the wind made the fishing bad.

At last, at nineteen minutes past six, father heron arrived, and walked to the nest in a stately manner with his plumes up. Mother did not display; perhaps she felt like me that he was late; she pecked absent-mindedly at a twig and left. Father worked his throat muscles and regurgitated breakfast into the bill of a baby, and then settled down to brood. Curiously enough, in nine minutes mother reappeared and presented her mate with a slender twig which he added to the nest, neither bird displaying; she turned and flew away and had not come back by seven o'clock. I went under the nest, and father peered silently down at me. On the ground were four large blue eggshells, for these birds do not carry eggshells away as do so many parents, but merely drop them over the edge of the nest.

Eight days later I had planned to go again. This morning I did not wake until 4:30, when I heard Purple Martins twittering and a Robin caroling; twelve minutes later I was backing out the car just as the Mockingbird was beginning his song, while Jupiter and a crescent moon shone in the east.

On the drive to the woods a Dickcissel rendered his earnest *jig jig jig-jig-jig*, and a Nighthawk gave its weird *peenk*.

As I made my way in the dim light through the woods, I was startled by a sudden loud snarl such as might properly come from a ferocious wildcat; but I recalled that I had heard it before and found its author to be a harmless Green Heron. This time I could see nothing and hurried on. I was happy to hear a Crested Flycatcher singing his "twilight song"—a very good song indeed for a bird whose usual utterances resemble shouts and grunts.

At the herons' I was much encouraged by the fact that father brought breakfast at seven minutes past five. This he dropped in the bottom of the nest; the children fluttered their wings appreciatively and rooted it up. Neither he nor his mate displayed. This good beginning, however, was deceptive; nothing else of special interest happened in the two hours that I stood there and fought mosquitoes. Mother returned to the home tree at 5:45 and stationed herself five feet from the nest; the young looked expectant and opened their bills, but soon subsided into the nest.

At 6:25 I thought something was surely going to happen, for mother shook herself, and all six babies appeared on top of the nest, stretched, flapped their wings and stepped about, one examining a twig; for ten minutes the nest was a scene of mild animation. Mother, however, merely preened herself a little; then at 6:38 stepped over to the nest and stood beside it, her offspring gathering hopefully about. A Red-shouldered Hawk screamed, and all the herons turned their heads in its direction, the young quickly disappearing. For the next half-hour they rested, only occasionally lifting a head, while mother stood like a statue beside them. From babyhood up the chief occupation of Yellow-crowned Night Herons appears to be complete immobility.

My last visit to the herons—from 6:30 to 7:30 in the evening of June 7—was a fitting climax in several ways. The first excitement came from a number of visiting Yellow-crowns that filled the woods with startling flaps and uncouth cries. These intrigued me so much that I attempted to give samples of them when I reached home, whereupon my baby objected, "Dat not pretty noise," and I think most people would agree with her.

I recorded no fewer than twenty different utterances showing great variability in pitch and tone. Some were sharp, even shrill—*wak, ick, ark, yeek.* The most common note was a gruff loud *owk,* which I variously described as harsh and angry, and sudden and disagreeable. There was a low, grunty *walk, walk, walk,* an annoyed *gowk, gowk,* and a squeaky *pedore.* Best of all was a deep and expressive *woe,* which at times was prolonged to *woe-ugh-ugh* and *woe-oh-oh.*

For forty minutes the young herons sat, the picture of patience, five on the nest and one near by. In their suits of brown, streaked and spotted with white, they resembled American Bitterns more than their own parents. Then father arrived and also waited, but when mother came both displayed so near to each other that she was bumped off the branch. He then bowed and whooped. The children climbed about on branches in their excitement, and then crowded into the nest; mother deposited supper there and they eagerly gobbled it up. Father performed once more, then flew away. I went under the nest for a farewell look, and mother objected in a grumbling tone—*wok-wok-wok.*

The owner of the woods wrote me that these herons raised a second family later in the season, of five, three hundred yards to the north, and the following year that there were no fewer than five pairs nesting in his woods. Perhaps some of these had been among the vociferous visitors that had so entertained me that June evening.

CHAPTER 18

Loti: The Tale of a Bobwhite

ONE June day some years ago thirteen little Bobwhites hatched out under a yellow bantam hen. They were tiny things, not much bigger than a person's thumb. So fascinating were they that it was necessary to look after them often that first day, for the shells had to be removed and the baby birds taken out and played with. They climbed around the nest and on my hands and lap, not realizing that the hen's excited cluckings meant, "Come, come, my children, eat this nice big corn," for they did not understand her language.

The next day they were taken from the fluffy, feathery bantam and put into a brooder. The poor little chicks missed her so much that they adopted my hand as the best mother they could find. Whenever I put it into the brooder they ran to it and cuddled under it, stretching up their heads and putting their bills in the cracks between my fingers. They were so entrancing that it was hard to do anything but play with them all the time. All thirteen could with some squeezing get under my hand and then they were perfectly content. When

I took them outdoors to hunt insects in the grass, they ran about awhile and then returned to my hand to cuddle.

Although they received the best of care, having plant lice, custard, ant eggs, and all sorts of insects to eat, on the fourth day two of the little birds walked about with their wings drooping and stretched from their bodies. In four days eleven died. I could not find the cause; perhaps they had become infected by some germ that was harmless to chickens inured to civilization, but fatal to little Bobwhites under the arti-

The Babies Were No Bigger than a Person's Thumb

ficial conditions of brooder life. The two left were healthy birds, but when they were nine days old one died from eating a sharp-pointed head of grass which pierced its crop. So then there was only one little Bobwhite; but he proved to be worth more to me than all his brothers and sisters could have been.

Being all alone in the world, he adopted me as mother, father, brother, and sister. When we went out walking, I would go ahead and the wee bird would follow in frantic haste until suddenly he spied something good to eat. Usually he was so much delayed by his discoveries that I would have to turn back to gather him up. He experimented on all sorts of things to see whether or not they were edible. When I lay down on the grass he liked to nestle in my hand, but best of all to explore my face, boring into my nostrils and ears, and once, when as an experiment I opened my mouth, popping into it! Nothing charmed him more than to burrow into ladies' long hair; it was the most like feathers of anything he knew.

The matter of a name for such a precious little bird received much thought; I tried one appellation after another, and before long hit upon one that suited me. Finding a louse upon him—evidently from the chicken house where I had taken him for daily weighings—I had to anoint his head with lard. This made him look like a Turkey Vulture, so I named him Zopiloti, the Mexican word for this creature.

The great excitement of Loti's life was eating. When he saw the can of fly larvae, mealworms, or miscellaneous insects, he could hardly contain himself—and tried to hop right into it. Although from the time he was ten days old he had always eaten alone and no one had ever taken any food from him, this had no effect on his instincts. Every piece of food was a prize that must be run off with as quickly as possible to a safe distance to be devoured. A dish of mealworms would be before him; he would seize one, hop off my lap, and rush away to eat it. Then he would come scurrying back for another and repeat the process six or eight times. Finally he would calm down and eat on the spot. If he dropped a mealworm he would have to jump down and get it, although there might be a bountiful supply before him. I suppose his ancestors had learned it was essential to make sure of every insect they started for—there wasn't always a kind Providence waiting with a canful.

Another funny trick of Loti's I accidentally discovered by putting my finger next him when he was eating. Immediately in alarm lest I should appropriate some of his precious insects, he began to push and crowd against my finger. This seems piggish, but is only natural in a bevy of little Bob-whites. Loti never learned that fingers did not eat his food; he always pushed and crowded when any one wanted to tease him in that way. Lady Bobwhites push their poor generous mates away when these have found something especially good and called them to it. Of course they need a great deal of nourishing food, since they must lay the eggs.

Loti had a sweet little voice and pretty baby notes; at four weeks he twittered and chattered all day long, but at eight weeks he talked less except when out foraging; then he kept up a steady stream of conversation—evidently the way that little Bobwhites keep together in grass that must often be over their heads. Whenever he found any of his favorite yellow sorrel in seed he would give in great excitement the note that I had thought meant, "Come, come, and eat this luscious thing," since grown Bobwhites give it, and particularly the males. Why a young bird should call others to his prize was a puzzle to me, for that was the last thing he really wanted. Apparently it meant merely, "Oh! What a wonderful thing to eat!" Whereupon in the usual situation wife and babies hurry to share in the feast.

Loti had been hatched on the farm of Dr. Clifton F. Hodge at Worcester, Massachusetts, but he spent much of his early youth at my home in Amherst, Massachusetts. It was here at the age of three months that he started to whistle *bob-white,* giving the call rather softly and usually when he was alone, but before long he gave it up. When he was four months old, he had all his adult feathers but was not quite as large as he grew to be later. He and I had now returned to Worcester and, thinking he must be lonely, I took him over to Dr. Hodge's to see his cousins six weeks younger than he, with the intention of bringing back several of them for company. But he and the young Bobwhites, still in juvenal plumage, did not seem to recognize each other as being in any way related.

It was a different matter, however, when we went to the pens of his uncles and aunts. There was the greatest excitement; every one wanted to fight. Uncle and aunt stood on the inside of the wire, puffed out and shouting as loud as they could, while their babies ran about unheeded, and Loti defied them on the outside, as puffed out as they and calling just as bad names. The uncles occasionally poked their heads out in their eagerness and then Loti pecked them. Since he ignored some of his relatives and fought the rest, I decided he might as well associate only with people until spring.

Loti and I had a large room to ourselves in the zoological laboratory at Clark University, while for sleeping quarters he had a roomy cage on a desk. Each morning he was happy to be let out; he would make little flights about a foot high, flapping his wings. He liked to crouch on the floor with his tail up in the air and then suddenly fly. At first he stayed closely by me, flying from the end of the long room to the door when he saw me going out. He would patter down the hall after me, waiting outside the dark storeroom, but liking to follow me into the light rooms. After a while he began to make expeditions of his own into the next room and did not follow me so well. He was constantly changing his ways.

Loti had a high sense of his own importance; when classes changed and a crowd of students poured out into the hall, he would rush in among them, oblivious of the danger of some one's stepping upon him. He always made a great oration on such occasions, and also whenever any one came into our room; this was evidently in the nature of a challenge and is called "caterwauling" in Herbert Stoddard's splendid monograph on the Bobwhite. He was friendly to every one, but liked some people much better than others. When visitors teased him by poking at him, he would retaliate with lowered head and open bill; his pecks could be vigorous when he was thoroughly roused.

Sometimes I took him on walks in the country, and he would follow me for a quarter of a mile at a time. He never strayed far from me out of doors; I believe he would have felt afraid if left alone in the open. One winter day Loti had his first experience with snow; he refused to walk in it and insisted on flying on to people's heads and shoulders and riding in state.

When I carried him in my hand through the town he was interested in many things and made many speeches. Dogs and roosters he disliked, but he was not much afraid of cats. Once when he was on the ground, he began to give alarm notes, and there was a wicked cat creeping up, and Loti, disturbed yet curious, walking straight towards her! Another day he and I were looking for grasshoppers; a Blue Jay screamed, and Loti rushed through the grass and hid in a ditch.

As spring came on Loti grew restless and naughty, pecking the noses of several of his admirers. On April 1st he began to whistle *bobwhite* after considerable encouragement from his friend Mr. W. A. Matheny who was able to imitate a number of phrases of Bobwhite vocabulary. Loti's usual *bobwhite* was ear-splittingly loud, but on occasion he gave it softly and prettily. Sometimes when he would be sitting quietly on my shoulder, Mr. Matheny would enter whistling; Loti would fly straight towards him, land on the cage, and stand there on tiptoe, with outspread wings and every feather erect, shouting his loudest, the very picture of defiance.

Although Loti considered people as his "social-companions," he never—as do many pet birds—looked for a "sex-companion" among human beings. Whether the fact that the first nine days of his life were spent with his brothers and sisters had anything to do with his reactions being only partially transferred to people, I do not know.

On April 13th we brought a mate for him—a young bird —from the farm; we named her Florence after our good friend Mrs. Matheny:

"We put her in Loti's cage. He puffs himself out and talks. She pays no attention to him. Later he tries to preen her, but she isn't responsive.

"April 14. Florence preens him, but he just tries to get out.

"April 15. Same situation. However, they sleep side by side.

"April 16. Both are happy and content together. Preen each other. Loti still likes very much to get out, and when he is away from her, Florence is most discontented."

On looking up the subject of courtship in Stoddard's book, I find that Loti did not give the proper "frontal display" of the ardent cock that presents a "vertical feathered wall" to his lady love. Loti never was a properly gallant Bobwhite husband.

Curiously enough Florence began to whistle *bobwhite* when separated from Loti, her whistle being intermediate in loudness between his two varieties. According to Stoddard it is most exceptional for hens to give this call. Both Loti and Florence belonged to the fourth generation raised in captivity, and some of their reactions may have been somewhat abnormal.

I had given the pair a nest box in late April, but they paid no attention to it until May 16th, when I found Florence inside, arranging the hay while Loti stood near by. Soon she came out picking up hay and throwing it over her back, slowly walking away. Loti went in and modeled the nest to suit himself, making pretty, soft, new noises, while Florence answered him with similar notes. About noon she laid her first egg, and the birds were even more excited, not being able to leave the nest and egg alone.

Florence laid an egg at two- and three-day intervals until her set reached twelve. Twice I noted her puffing herself out and giving the food call to the eggs.

"June 6. Loti pays no more attention to the eggs or nest, but is very fond of Florence. He even begins to be a bit gallant. He gives Florence a worm, and thinks of giving her a spider, but finally eats it himself."

Then something strange happened. On June 8th the pair had been most affectionate, standing side by side almost all day. On the 9th, however, when I returned to my room from a lecture, Florence was crouched in a corner and Loti was craning his neck at her and giving the alarm note. She spent all her time hiding in corners, and when routed out from one would rush to another. She ate and drank little, even though I put food and water beside her. She seemed terrified of Loti, while he was entirely indifferent to her. He began to act like a bachelor, standing in the window nearly all day whistling *bobwhite,* and trying to get out. After four or five days Florence calmed down, but she and Loti avoided each other. My only theory as to the origin of this sudden quarrel was that the birds must have suffered a severe fright during my absence from the room.

On June 17th I brought them to Grey Rocks and established them in a large outdoor cage. Here Florence made a nest and in July laid a second set of twelve eggs, but as happened with most of the Bobwhites in captivity, she failed to incubate either set. Her eggs were sent to the State Game Farm near Worcester; the first set hatched well, but all of the last were infertile. Florence and Loti became friends again, but not mates; on July 6th they were again sleeping side by side. Loti whistled *bobwhite* a good deal, and Florence did the same one day when I started to take him off for a walk. Loti was as tame as ever, but he was no longer affectionate; he fought the feet of all men who came near, and when taken into my hand would struggle to get loose. One day in September the door of the pen was left open by mistake; the birds wandered out and a cat pounced on Florence.

Loti was brought into the house and once more was the cunningest pet imaginable, following me everywhere and loving to sit on my shoulder. If I happened to lie down, up he would fly on top of me, sometimes lying down peacefully, but at other times determined to preen my hair and eyebrows. Bobwhites preen each other's heads and chins, so Loti preened us and in turn liked to be stroked under his chin; he would shut his eyes and put his head far back or away over to one side. If I tossed him onto the floor, back he would fly the next instant, for he seemed to think it the finest kind of play. He liked to cuddle between my feet when I was washing dishes; this was a dangerous position, for I would forget him and step on his toes. The unwise little bird would squeal and peck my feet, but still he would stay.

He discovered that steam radiators were pleasant places to lie under. He was always experimenting with objects, tweaking paper, pencils, and pens, and throwing buttons out of the sewing basket; but I could never persuade him to put a single one back! He tasted and seemed to like such queer things as mucilage, library paste, cold cream, and ink. There were many civilized dishes of which he was fond, such as bread, crackers, butter, scrambled eggs, apple sauce, mashed potatoes, brown sugar, and sweet chocolate; yet he would never taste meat.

Loti was not especially fond of my husband—perhaps he

was a bit jealous—and often greeted his home-coming by attacking his feet. When he became troublesome my husband would show him the broom or the mop, and Loti would turn tail in a hurry. As evening came on and the gas was lighted, Loti never acted as he did in the daytime; he would persist in flying on people's heads, so he was always put to bed early. When he was in his cage at night, if he heard any one singing, he would accompany the music with a mournful, long drawn-out note.

I wish I might have chronicled a long and happy life for Loti. To our grief he died by accident one day in March. We sorely missed the busy, cheerful little bird, for his affectionate and winning ways had greatly endeared him to our hearts.

CHAPTER 19

Spring in Oklahoma

IN THE thirteen years in which our family lived in Oklahoma, we had grown to love the state, and it was with happy anticipation in late April, 1937, that my daughter Constance and I left a bleak Chicago to study once more Oklahoma birds and flowers.

The trip through Illinois was a monotonous succession of plowed fields, but in Missouri we found a country of hills and woods, budding with delicate new leaves. Mile after mile the hillsides glowed with the pink of the redbud; no cherry orchard in Japan could have been more exquisite. Along the roadside and railroad right of way bloomed patches of wild strawberries, little pink and white spring beauties, tiny wild pansies, and gleaming thousands of golden buttercups. Here a hillside was blue with Quaker ladies, there one was white with Nothoscordum. Tantalizing glimpses of a violet too blue for wood sorrel and too low for phlox induced us to stop the car; we were thrilled to recognize the bird-foot violet, not only the usual form, but also the bicolored variety with its upper petals of deep purple.

Farther south it was the immaculate white of the dogwood

which contrasted with the sandstone cliffs, the pink new leaves of the oaks and the smoky grey of the woods. The dogwood, unlike many imported shrubs, has no dowdy season; its bark and branches form attractive silhouettes in the winter, its flowers are famous, its summer foliage handsome, and in the fall it produces not only scarlet berries for people and birds to enjoy, but crimson leaves besides. Yet in some "scientifically" managed forests the dogwood is cut out as a "weed tree"!

Northeastern Oklahoma lies in the Ozarks and is covered with oak-hickory forests and some yellow pine. The inhabitants live by lumbering and pasturing the woods; gardens are fenced, and cattle, horses, and pigs roam free. Because of the custom of burning over the woods each spring, in the mistaken belief that it improves the pasture, the humus is destroyed and the pines prevented from replacing themselves. On one hilltop we found a Pine Warbler bravely proclaiming territory from an oak. His pines lay about in log piles and brush heaps. He must have settled there before the pines were cut, and was loath to leave his home after their destruction.

We passed through a hilly oak savanna where the ground was often covered with a mist of blue phacelia. Wild hyacinths, both the pale edible kind and the poisonous species, grew among the rocks. South of Sallisaw we crossed the new bridge onto a track through a last year's cotton field that led to a prairie adorned with patch after patch of scarlet painted cup, little blue daisies, toadflax, Venus' looking-glass, a dark purple phacelia, and on each of the many low Indian mounds (formed by the collapse of prehistoric huts), a golden thatch of corydalis. We hope it will not be spoiled when the road is put through; there is something about a main highway that only too often blights natural beauty.

Egret and Anhinga

On reaching the southeastern corner of Oklahoma where the southern cypress swamps extend a few miles into the state, we settled in a camp by Mountain Fork, not far from the largest tree in the state, a venerable cypress. We talked birds with the owner of the camp and were excited to hear that "White Cranes" were to be found nesting in the cypress "brakes." Our informant agreed to guide us to the "Buzzards' Roost Cypress Brake," and so we drove through the woods for some seven miles, through loblolly pines, and then hardwoods–southern trees that seemed strange to us–sweet gums, willow oaks, water oaks, and giant hollies in bloom. It was odd to find Catbirds in such a wild place, their companions Cerulean and Parula Warblers, and the absurd White-eyed Vireo. After a long, hot tramp, we began to hear grunts and barks and yaps, and at last came to the brakes, which are not swamps, but shallow lakes in which the cypress stand. We saw more "Buzzards" at first than Great Blue Herons, but soon began to make out the nests in the great cypresses with the statuesque birds upon them. All at once I saw a long-necked, long-tailed, snaky-looking fowl slip off a nest.

"Anhinga!" I shouted in the wildest excitement. All of us were wading by this time, although only I was provided with boots. Soon the water gushed in over my boot tops, and the guide and I climbed upon a cypress log and perched there, while Constance waded boldly on across the brake through water that came above her waist. Although she saw no snakes (they escape if they are aware of human approach), two weeks later Hugh Davis of the Tulsa Zoo caught in this very spot the largest cottonmouth water moccasin he had ever found in Oklahoma. It was a female measuring four feet long and as thick as a man's arm.

"See the White Crane," said the guide, and there was a wonderful American Egret on its nest, the first nesting record for Oklahoma. The air was filled with big birds—Great Blue Herons, Turkey Vultures, and Black Vultures. And then the Anhingas appeared, sailing overhead with their queer turkey-like tails outspread. Only once before had this species been recorded for the state, and here we found it nesting! Occasionally an Egret circled above, translucent white in contrast to the black of the Vultures and grey of the Great Blue Herons. Near us a quiet pair of Yellow-crowned Night Herons stood on their nests.

Cypresses are the most graceful of conifers—smooth trunks, then, fifty feet up, the open branches terminated by pale green lacelike twigs. Our host said that he had counted over fifteen hundred rings on some of the logs brought to his shingling mill. There are few young cypresses; when the veterans are cut—and this is done even where they are essential for holding the stream bank—they are not replaced. And the price of these magnificent trees, as shingle material, is two dollars an acre!

The next day our guide took us to another beautiful woods in which for many years there had been a large heronry of the Egrets, but which the summer before had been cut out when the young were in the nests—the only season when the water is low enough for the lumbermen to work. Not an Egret had returned to nest in the remnants of their cypresses.

An inadvertent remark of our guide revealed the fact that "our" heronry was to be logged within a month! As soon as we reached the University of Oklahoma, we consulted with Dr. Paul Sears, head of the Botany Department, who advised talking with our old friend, Dr. Charles Gould of the National Park Service. He interested Mr. A. R. Reaves, head of the State Park Board, at whose request the owner of the land agreed not to cut the timber, until it was found whether money could be obtained to purchase the brake for the state.

The Tulsa Audubon Society is trying to raise money for that purchase partly by the sale of superb photographs of the Herons and Anhingas taken by Hugh Davis. The "Buzzards' Roost Brake" has gained at least a reprieve from its death sentence.

Reluctantly leaving the uninhabited bottoms of Mountain Fork River and driving west, we encountered in a field beyond Hugo our beloved Scissor-tailed Flycatchers. Shouting *pup pup perleep,* they flung themselves yards into the air, displaying the rose patch beneath the wings, and opening and closing their long forked tails. The meadow resembled one of Fra Angelico's flower-spangled Paradises; the flowers were so numerous that there was scarcely space for grass: sky-blue flax, yellow flax, little pinkish western daisies, white beard-tongue with trumpets twice the size of Canterbury bells, and sheet upon sheet of scarlet painted cup and magenta Indian blanket. In this flowery expanse the Dickcissels, dressed like miniature Meadowlarks, staked out their claims and defied their neighbors; *jig jig jig-jig-jig* resounded on all sides. Migrating Clay-colored Sparrows gave their funny little songs, while Grasshopper Sparrows, thoroughly at home in this unbroken prairie, buzzed industriously. From a near-by thicket sounded the quaint refrain of a Bell Vireo.

Passing through the blackjack oaks of central Oklahoma, we entered the prairies of the northwest. Normally much less luxuriant than those of eastern Oklahoma, they had been suffering from a succession of droughts, being as brown in May as they usually are in August. Farmers told us that much of the rich buffalo grass has been destroyed in the last few years by the cattle. Depressed by the monotony and barrenness of the main highways (the builders have developed a practice of shearing off the prairie banks to leave a smooth expanse of raw earth which is cut to pieces by the first rain), we turned to the side roads. Here we discovered more towns of the cheerful little prairie dogs than we feared had survived; with their staccato barks and jerking tails these sociable marmots are one of the most amusing of western sights. Recent research has shown that rodents in the West perform the work of earthworms in the moister East, stirring, aerating, and fertilizing the soil which the herds pack down. They do not become pests unless the native predators have been exterminated. Yet the Biological Survey conducts campaigns of wholesale poisoning against them!

Crossing the South Canadian on a concrete bridge at Taloga, we noticed Cliff Swallows below us. Their jug-shaped mud nests were huddled against one another under the bridge. Groups of the birds, fluttering on the sand like so many dark butterflies, gathered material for their nests from a small patch of mud. The river, like others in this region, consisted of a shallow stream meandering through a vast sand plain. Within a week torrential rains broke the drought and, filling the river bed from bank to bank, tore out this great bridge. When rain does fall in this overgrazed and overcultivated country, there is little to hold it in the soil.

How little droughts affect the prairie when it is not overburdened with stock can be seen by comparing the high, luxuriant grass and thick sod of the buffalo pasture in the Wichita National Forest with the scattered bunches of grass surrounded by bare earth and cactus in the cattle range beyond the fence. In this austere country the native prairie through thousands of years of wind and drought has been able to maintain itself and produce a surplus for grazing animals. When the pasture is overstocked, the more nutritious grasses are destroyed, to be replaced with cacti and weeds; the ground is unprotected by sod, and heavy rains wash away the fertile topsoil.

Plowing of the uplands is even more disastrous. Wheat drains the moisture and fertility from the soil and does not protect it from water and wind erosion. In a few years a good pasture becomes a mass of drifting sand, on which even weeds can hardly live. Such wastes are often separated merely by a barbed-wire fence from fairly good pasture land. The southwestern farmers, as Dr. Sears describes them in his book, *Deserts on the March,* each year are extending the boundaries of the desert eastward.

In hopes of finding the Mississippi Kites nesting and the Lesser Prairie Chicken booming, we drove next day from Arnett to the Davidson Brothers' ranch. Although this sandy upland used to be grass-covered, the original round "shinneries" composed of dozens of little oaks fifteen or perhaps only ten feet high, now spring from a perfect sea of miniature oaks. On foot one gets the curious effect of walking in an oak forest only a foot or two high. With the drought and overstocking of cattle, the oaks have simply replaced the grass.

At noon under an overcast sky the Chickens, that normally "dance" only at dawn and dusk, were cackling and booming from many ridges. Although the birds were comparatively tame, when we drove the car through the shinnery right up to them, they took to the air with a slow, straight flight and coasted down to the next ridge or crouched and peered at us over the dwarf oaks. Turning back to a knoll where we had noticed a pair of the pretty white Mississippi Kites, we discovered their nest lined with green leaves near the top of a ten-foot shin oak. It is a pleasure to find these graceful and beneficial birds abundant in some places in northwestern Oklahoma.

Driving farther, despite showers, through this interesting ranch, where wild life is protected, we were passing through an open pasture when a Prairie Hen crossed the track ahead of us. We stopped the car, and saw that she was followed by three cocks. A Prairie Chicken ordinarily resembles a Plymouth Rock hen done in brown and tan, and he is hardly distinguishable from the surrounding prairie. But when he sets out to impress the neighbors, what a difference!

Each cock selected a piece of ground about twenty-five feet from the car and about two-thirds that distance from his rivals and began. He spread his orange eyebrows till his whole head seemed orange, raised and spread his tail, which was white beneath, lowered his wings like a turkey cock, inflated the reddish sacs on each side of his neck, raised his neck tufts till they met above his head, and lowered his head, so that he seemed to have a tail at each end. Thus extraordinarily transformed, he began to "dance" in the manner of an Indian warrior, making short rushes, then stamping in place till his whole body quivered, meanwhile uttering a variety of clucks, chuckles, and other strange notes. At the climax of his excitement he jerked his head down twice uttering a sound like *woo-loo,* the booming that can be heard a distance of two miles.

Once two displaying cocks rushed towards each other, then crouched in the grass, defying each other in choice language, but did not actually come to blows. Sometimes the cocks would leap a few feet into the air, cackling like barnyard fowls. The hen, in the meantime, continued to nibble here and there, apparently ignoring the cocks, that followed her as she progressed across the prairie. After an hour's enjoyment of the show from the car, we stepped out, and the birds immediately took to flight.

These thrilling performances were common sights in the days of early settlement, for the Prairie Chicken is a bird not of the wilderness, but of savanna and farm land. If they were given reasonable protection, thev would become abundant once more throughout the Great Plains. This world would be a far lovelier and more wonderful place to live in, if we left some space for the wild creatures, some forests for the beasts and birds, some swamps for the wild fowl, some prairie for the wild flowers.

It sometimes seems from the way people treat this beautiful earth, as if they expected the end of the world to come shortly, perhaps in the year 2000. On the contrary, scientists tell us that the earth should remain habitable to man for *twelve thousand million years!* What, unless we mend our ways, will there be left of interest and variety, of beauty and unspoiled wilderness, in that inconceivably long stretch of years to come?

REFERENCES

Chapter 1

ALTUM, BERNARD, *Der Vogel und sein Leben.* Münster, 1868. 168 pp.

HOWARD, H. ELIOT, *Territory in Bird Life.* London, 1920. 308 pp.

MAYR, ERNST, "Bernard Altum and the Territory Theory." *Proceedings Linnaean Society of New York,* (1935), Nos. 45, 46. 15 pp.

NICE, MARGARET M., "The Theory of Territorialism and Its Development." Fifty Years' Progress of American Ornithology, pp. 89–100. Lancaster, (1933).

Chapter 2

HEINROTH, OSCAR and MAGDALENA. *Die Vögel Mitteleuropas in allen Lebens- und Entwicklungstufen photographisch aufgenommen und in ihrem Seelenleben bei der Aufzucht vom Ei ab beobachtet.* IV. Band: Nachtrag. Berlin (Hugo Bermühler) 1931–1933. 4° 128 pp., 30 Bunttaflen 72 Schwarztafeln.

Chapter 7

BALDWIN, S. PRENTISS, "The Marriage Relations of the House Wren." *The Auk,* 38:228–237 (1921).

Chapter 10

NICE, MARGARET M., *Studies in the Life History of the Song Sparrow,* Part I. Trans. Linnaean Society of New York, Vol. IV, 1937 (247 pp.). Dover reprint, 1964.

Chapter 11

FRIEDMANN, HERBERT, *The Cowbirds.* Springfield, Ill., 1929. 421 pp.

HANN, HARRY W., "Life-History of the Ovenbird in Southern Michigan." *Wilson Bulletin,* 49:145–237 (1937).

O'NEAL, R. J., "A Word for the Cowbird." *Bird-Lore,* 11:214–215 (1909).

RAND, F. L., in Friedmann's *Cowbirds,* p. 184.

WIDMANN, OTTO, *A Preliminary Catalog of the Birds of Missouri* (288 pp.). Trans. Academy of St. Louis, Vol. XVII (1907).

WILSON, ALEXANDER, *American Ornithology,* Vol. I. Philadelphia, 1808. 158 pp.

Chapter 12

MOUSLEY, HENRY, "A Study of the Home Life of the Northern Parula and Other Warblers at Hatley, Stanstead County, Quebec, 1921–1922." *The Auk,* 41:263–288 (1924).

Chapter 14

MOUSLEY, HENRY, "A Further Study of the Home Life of the Northern Parula, and of the Yellow Warbler and Ovenbird." *The Auk,* 43:184–197 (1926).

Chapter 16

CRAIG, WALLACE, "The Expressions of Emotion in the Pigeons: II–The Mourning Dove *(Zenaidura macroura* Linn.)." *The Auk,* 28:398–407 (1911).

Chapter 18

STODDARD, HERBERT, *The Bobwhite Quail.* New York, 1931.

Chapter 19

SEARS, PAUL B., *Deserts on the March.* Norman, Okla., 1935.

SUMNER, FRANCIS B., "The Need for a More Serious Effort to Rescue a Few Fragments of Vanishing Nature." *Scientific Monthly,* 10:238–248 (March, 1920).

VOGT, WILLIAM, *Thirst on the Land: A Plea for Water Conservation for the Benefit of Man and Wild Life.* National Association of Audubon Societies Circular No. 32, 1937. 32 pp.

SCIENTIFIC NAMES OF BIRDS MENTIONED IN THE TEXT

Acadian Flycatcher, *Empidonax virescens*
American Egret, *Casmerodius albus egretta*
Anhinga, or Water-Turkey, *Anhinga anhinga*
Baltimore Oriole, *Icterus galbula*
Barred Owl, *Strix varia*
Bell Vireo, *Vireo belli belli*
Bewick Wren, *Thryomanes bewicki*
Black and White Warbler, *Mniotilta varia*
Black-throated Blue Warbler, *Dendroica caerulescens*
Black-throated Green Warbler, *Dendroica virens*
Black Vulture, *Coragyps atratus*
Blackburnian Warbler, *Dendroica fusca*
Blue-grey Gnatcatcher, *Polioptila caerulea*
Blue Jay, *Cyanocitta cristata*
Bobolink, *Dolichonyx oryzivorus*
Bobwhite, *Colinus virginianus*
Bronzed Grackle, *Quiscalus quiscula aeneus*
Brown Thrasher, *Toxostoma rufum*
Cardinal, *Richmondena cardinalis*
Catbird, *Dumetella carolinensis*
Cerulean Warbler, *Dendroica cerulea*
Chestnut-sided Warbler, *Dendroica pensylvanica*
Chewink, *Pipilo erythrophthalmus*
Chickadee, *Penthestes atricapillus*
Clay-colored Sparrow, *Spizella pallida*
Cliff Swallow, *Petrochelidon albifrons*
Cowbird, *Molothrus ater*
Crested Flycatcher, *Myiarchus crinitus*
Dickcissel, *Spiza americana*
Downy Woodpecker, *Dryobates pubescens*
English Sparrow, *Passer domesticus*
European Cuckoo, *Cuculus canorus*

Field Sparrow, *Spizella pusilla*
Goldfinch, *Spinus tristis*
Grasshopper Sparrow, *Ammodramus savannarum*
Great Blue Heron, *Ardea herodias*
Green Heron, *Butorides virescens*
Hermit Thrush, *Hylocichla guttata*
House Finch, *Carpodacus mexicanus frontalis*
House Wren, *Troglodytes aedon*
Indigo Bunting, *Passerina cyanea*
Junco, *Junco hyemalis*
Lark Sparrow, *Chondestes grammacus*
Lesser Prairie Chicken, *Tympanuchus pallidicinctus*
Lincoln Sparrow, *Melospiza lincolni*
Magnolia Warbler, *Dendroica magnolia*
Maryland Yellowthroat, *Geothlypis trichas*
Meadow Lark, *Sturnella magna*
Mississippi Kite, *Ictinia misisippiensis*
Mockingbird, *Mimus polyglottos*
Mourning Dove, *Zenaidura macroura*
Myrtle Warbler, *Dendroica coronata*
Orchard Oriole, *Icterus spurius*
Ovenbird, *Seiurus aurocapillus*
Parula Warbler, *Compsothlypis americana*
Phoebe, *Sayornis phoebe*
Pileated Woodpecker, *Ceophloeus pileatus*
Plumbeous Chickadee, *Penthestes carolinensis agilis*
Prothonotary Warbler, *Protonotaria citrea*
Purple Finch, *Carpodacus purpureus*
Purple Martin, *Progne subis subis*
Red-bellied Woodpecker, *Centurus carolinus*
Red-eyed Vireo, *Vireo olivaceus*
Red-shouldered Hawk, *Buteo lineatus*
Red-winged Blackbird, *Agelaius phoeniceus*
Robin, *Turdus migratorius*
Ruby-crowned Kinglet, *Corthylio calendula*
Scarlet Tanager, *Piranga erythromelas*
Scissor-tailed Flycatcher, *Muscivora forficata*
Song Sparrow, *Melospiza melodia*
Swainson Hawk, *Buteo swainsoni*

Scientific Names of Birds Mentioned in the Text

Sycamore Warbler, *Dendroica dominica albilora*
Tree Sparrow, *Spizella arborea*
Tufted Titmouse, *Baeolophus bicolor*
Turkey Vulture, *Cathartes aura septentrionalis*
Warbling Vireo, *Vireo gilvus*
White-crowned Sparrow, *Zontrichia leucophrys*
Wood Pewee, *Myiochanes virens*
Wood Thrush, *Hylocichla mustelina*
Wren Tit, *Chamaea fasciata*
Yellow-breasted Chat, *Icteria virens*
Yellow-crowned Night Heron, *Nyctanassa violacea*
Yellow Warbler, *Dendroica aestiva*

CATALOGUE OF DOVER BOOKS

Nature

AN INTRODUCTION TO BIRD LIFE FOR BIRD WATCHERS, Aretas A. Saunders. Fine, readable introduction to birdwatching. Includes a great deal of basic information on about 160 different varieties of wild birds—elementary facts not easily found elsewhere. Complete guide to identification procedures, methods of observation, important habits of birds, finding nests, food, etc. "Could make bird watchers of readers who never suspected they were vulnerable to that particular virus," CHICAGO SUNDAY TRIBUNE. Unabridged, corrected edition. Bibliography. Index. 22 line drawings by D. D'Ostilio. Formerly "The Lives of Wild Birds." 256pp. 5⅜ x 8½. T1139 Paperbound **$1.00**

LIFE HISTORIES OF NORTH AMERICAN BIRDS, Arthur Cleveland Bent. Bent's historic, all-encompassing series on North American birds, originally produced under the auspices of the Smithsonian Institution, now being republished in its entirety by Dover Publications. The twenty-volume collection forms the most comprehensive, most complete, most-used source of information in existence. Each study describes in detail the characteristics, range, distribution, habits, migratory patterns, courtship procedures, plumage, eggs, voice, enemies, etc. of the different species and subspecies of the birds that inhabit our continent, utilizing reports of hundreds of contemporary observers as well as the writings of the great naturalists of the past. Invaluable to the ornithologist, conservationist, amateur naturalist, and birdwatcher. All books in the series contain numerous photographs to provide handy guides for identification and study.

LIFE HISTORIES OF NORTH AMERICAN BIRDS OF PREY. Including hawks, eagles, falcons, buzzards, condors, owls, etc. Index. Bibliographies of 923 items. 197 full-page plates containing close to 400 photographs. Total of 907pp. 5⅜ x 8½.
Vol. I: T931 Paperbound **$2.50**
Vol. II: T932 Paperbound **$2.50**
The set Paperbound **$5.00**

LIFE HISTORIES OF NORTH AMERICAN SHORE BIRDS. Including 81 varieties of such birds as sandpipers, woodcocks, snipes, phalaropes, oyster catchers, and many others. Index for each volume. Bibliographies of 449 entries. 121 full-page plates including over 200 photographs. Total of 860 pp. 5⅜ x 8½.
Vol. I: T933 Paperbound **$2.35**
Vol. II: T934 Paperbound **$2.35**
The set Paperbound **$4.70**

LIFE HISTORIES OF NORTH AMERICAN WILD FOWL. Including 73 varieties of ducks, geese, mergansers, swans, etc. Index for each volume. Bibliographies of 268 items. 106 full-page plates containing close to 200 photographs. Total of 685pp. 5⅜ x 8½.
Vol. I: T285 Paperbound **$2.50**
Vol. II: T286 Paperbound **$2.50**
The set Paperbound **$5.00**

LIFE HISTORIES OF NORTH AMERICAN GULLS AND TERNS. 50 different varieties of gulls and terns. Index. Bibliography. 93 plates including 149 photographs. xii + 337pp. 5⅜ x 8½. T1029 Paperbound **$2.75**

LIFE HISTORIES OF NORTH AMERICAN GALLINACEOUS BIRDS. Including partridge, quail, grouse, pheasant, pigeons, doves, and others. Index. Bibliography. 93 full-page plates including 170 photographs. xiii + 490pp. 5⅜ x 8½. T1028 Paperbound **$2.75**

THE MALAY ARCHIPELAGO, Alfred Russel Wallace. The record of the explorations (8 years, 14,000 miles) of the Malay Archipelago by a great scientific observer. A contemporary of Darwin, Wallace independently arrived at the concept of evolution by natural selection, applied the new theories of evolution to later genetic discoveries, and made significant contributions to biology, zoology, and botany. This work is still one of the classics of natural history and travel. It contains the author's reports of the different native peoples of the islands, descriptions of the island groupings, his accounts of the animals, birds, and insects that flourished in this area. The reader is carried through strange lands, alien cultures, and new theories, and will share in an exciting, unrivalled travel experience. Unabridged reprint of the 1922 edition, with 62 drawings and maps. 3 appendices, one on cranial measurements. xvii + 515pp. 5⅜ x 8. T187 Paperbound **$2.00**

THE TRAVELS OF WILLIAM BARTRAM, edited by **Mark Van Doren.** This famous source-book of American anthropology, natural history, geography is the record kept by Bartram in the 1770's, on travels through the wilderness of Florida, Georgia, the Carolinas. Containing accurate and beautiful descriptions of Indians, settlers, fauna, flora, it is one of the finest pieces of Americana ever written. Introduction by Mark Van Doren. 13 original illustrations. Index. 448pp. 5⅜ x 8. T13 Paperbound **$2.00**

COMMON SPIDERS OF THE UNITED STATES, J. H. Emerton. Only non-technical, but thorough, reliable guide to spiders for the layman. Over 200 spiders from all parts of the country, arranged by scientific classification, are identified by shape and color, number of eyes, habitat and range, habits, etc. Full text, 501 line drawings and photographs, and valuable introduction explain webs, poisons, threads, capturing and preserving spiders, etc. Index. New synoptic key by S. W. Frost. xxiv + 225pp. 5⅜ x 8. T223 Paperbound **$1.45**

LIFE HISTORIES OF NORTH AMERICAN MARSH BIRDS. A wealth of data on 54 different kinds of marsh bird (flamingo, ibis, bittern, heron, egret, crane, crake, rail, coot, etc.). Index. Bibliography. 98 full-page plates containing 179 black-and-white photographs. xiv + 392pp. 5⅜ x 8½. T1082 Paperbound **$2.75**

LIFE HISTORIES OF NORTH AMERICAN DIVING BIRDS. Thirty-six different diving birds including grebe, loon, auk, murre, puffin, and the like. Index. Bibliography. 55 full-page plates (92 photographs). xiv + 239pp. 5⅜ x 8½. T1091 Paperbound **$2.75**

LIFE HISTORIES OF NORTH AMERICAN WOOD WARBLERS. Covers about 58 types. Index. Bibliography. 83 full-page plates containing 125 black-and-white photographs. xi + 734pp. of text. 5⅜ x 8½.
Vol. I: T1153 Paperbound **$2.50**
Vol. II: T1154 Paperbound **$2.50**
The set Paperbound **$5.00**

LIFE HISTORIES OF NORTH AMERICAN FLYCATCHERS, LARKS, SWALLOWS, AND THEIR ALLIES. Complete information on about 78 different varieties. Index. Bibliography. 70 full-page plates (117 photographs). xi + 555pp. of text. 5⅜ x 8½. T1090 Paperbound **$2.75**

AMERICAN WILDLIFE, AND PLANTS: A GUIDE TO WILDLIFE FOOD HABITS, A. C. Martin, H. S. Zim, A. L. Nelson. Result of 75 years of research by U. S. Fish and Wildlife Service into food and feeding habits of more than 1,000 species of birds and mammals, their distribution in America, migratory habits, and the most important plant-animal relationships. Treats over 300 common species of birds, fur and game animals, small mammals, hoofed browsers, fish, amphibians, reptiles by group, giving data on their food, ranges, habits and economies. Also focuses on the different genera of plants that furnish food for our wildlife, animals that use them, and their value. Only thorough study of its kind in existence. "Of immense value to sportsmen, naturalists, bird students, foresters, landscape architects, botanists," NATURE. "Undoubtedly an essential handbook," SCIENTIFIC MONTHLY. Unabridged republication of 1951 edition. Over 600 illustrations, maps, etc. Classified bibliography. Index. x + 500pp. 5⅜ x 8. T793 Paperbound **$2.50**

HOW TO KNOW THE WILD FLOWERS, Mrs. Wm. Starr Dana. A Guide to the names, haunts, and habits of wild flowers. Well-known classic of nature lore. Informative and delightful. Plants classified by color and season of their typical flowers for easy identification. Thorough coverage of more than 1,000 important flowering, berry-bearing and foliage plants of Eastern and Central United States and Canada. Complete botanical information about each important plant. Also history, uses, folklore, habitat, etc. Nomenclature modernized by C. J. Hylander. 174 full-page illustrations by Marion Satterlee. xii + 481pp. 5⅜ x 8½.
T332 Paperbound **$2.00**

HOW PLANTS GET THEIR NAMES, L. H. Bailey. Introduction to botanical nomenclature for the horticulturist and garden-lover. Discussions of Carl Linnaeus, "father of botany," and analysis of his definitions of genus and species, a brief history of the science before Linnaean systematization, a chapter on plant identification, a mine of information on the rules of nomenclature and Latin stems and word-endings used in botanical nomenclature, with pronunciation guides. An important section contains a full list of generic terms of horticultural literature and common Latin words and their English botanical applications and meanings. "Written with knowledge and authority, charm and eloquence and poetic imagination on the varied aspects of the author's specialty," New York Times. 11 illustrations. vi + 181pp. 5⅜ x 8½. T796 Paperbound **$1.25**

THE CACTACEAE: DESCRIPTIONS AND ILLUSTRATIONS OF PLANTS OF THE CACTUS FAMILY, N. L. Britton and J. N. Rose. Definitive study of plants of the Cactus Family. The authors devoted more than 15 years of research to this monumental task and produced an exhaustive, rigorously scientific account never likely to be superseded. 3 major classifications, or tribes, are recognized, under which they arrange and describe in full detail 124 genera and 1,235 species of cactus from all over the world. Complete data on each species: leaves, flowers, seeds, fruit, distribution, growth, spines, stem structure, economic uses, etc. In addition, 125 keys facilitate identification of genera and species. For teachers and students of botany and forestry, naturalists, conservationists, and nature lovers, this is an indispensable work. Unabridged republication of second (1937) edition. First edition originally published under the auspices of the Carnegie Institution, Washington, D.C. 4 vols. bound as 2. 1279 illustrations, photographs, sketches, etc. 137 plates. Total of xxvii + 1039pp. 8 x 10¼. T771 Clothbound, 2-volume set **$20.00**

GUIDE TO SOUTHERN TREES, Elwood S. and J. George Harrar. A handy, comprehensive 700-page manual with numerous illustrations and information on more than 350 different kinds of trees, covering the entire area south of the Mason-Dixon line from the Atlantic Ocean to the Florida Keys and western Texas. Descriptions range from the common pine, cypress, walnut, beech, and elm to such rare species as Franklinia, etc. A mine of information on leaves, flowers, twigs, bark, fruit, distribution etc. of each kind of tree. Eminently readable, written in non-technical language, it is an indispensable handbook for all lovers of the outdoors. Revised edition. Index. 81-item bibliography. Glossary. 200 full-page illustrations. ix + 709pp. 4⅝ x 6⅜. T945 Paperbound **$2.35**

WESTERN FOREST TREES, James B. Berry. For years a standard guide to the trees of the Western United States. Covers over 70 different subspecies, ranging from the Pacific shores to western South Dakota, New Mexico, etc. Much information on range and distribution, growth habits,. appearance, leaves, bark, fruit, twigs, etc. for each tree discussed, plus material on wood of the trees and its uses. Basic division (Trees with needle-like leaves, scale-like leaves, and compound, lobed or divided, and simple broadleaf trees), along with almost 100 illustrations (mostly full-size) of buds, leaves, etc., aids in easy identification of just about any tree of the area. Many subsidiary keys. Revised edition. Introduction. 12 photos. 85 illustrations by Mary E. Eaton. Index. xii + 212pp. 5⅜ x 8.
T1138 Paperbound **$1.35**

MANUAL OF THE TREES OF NORTH AMERICA (EXCLUSIVE OF MEXICO), Charles Sprague Sargent. The magnum opus of the greatest American dendrologist. Based on 44 years of original research, this monumental work is still the most comprehensive and reliable sourcebook on the subject. Includes 185 genera and 717 species of trees (and many shrubs) found in the U.S., Canada, and Alaska. 783 illustrative drawings by C. E. Faxon and Mary W. Gill. An all-encompassing lifetime reference book for students, teachers of botany and forestry, naturalists, conservationists, and all nature lovers. Includes an 11-page analytical key to genera to help the beginner locate any tree by its leaf characteristics. Within the text over 100 further keys aid in easy identification. Synopsis of families. Glossary. Index. 783 illustrations, 1 map. Total of 1 + 891pp. 5⅜ x 8.
T277 Vol. I Paperbound **$2.25**
T278 Vol. II Paperbound **$2.25**
The set **$4.50**

TREES OF THE EASTERN AND CENTRAL UNITED STATES AND CANADA, W. M. Harlow, Professor of Wood Technology, College of Forestry, State University of N. Y., Syracuse, N. Y. This middle-level text is a serious work covering more than 140 native trees and important escapes, with information on general appearance, growth habit, leaf forms, flowers, fruit, bark, and other features. Commercial use, distribution, habitat, and woodlore are also given. Keys within the text enable you to locate various species with ease. With this book you can identify at sight almost any tree you are likely to encounter; you will know which trees have edible fruit, which are suitable for house planting, and much other useful and interesting information. More than 600 photographs and figures. xiii + 288pp. 4⅝ x 6½.
T395 Paperbound **$1.35**

FRUIT KEY AND TWIG KEY TO TREES AND SHRUBS (FRUIT KEY TO NORTHEASTERN TREES, TWIG TREE TO DECIDUOUS WOODY PLANTS OF EASTERN NORTH AMERICA), W. M. Harlow. The only guides with photographs of every twig and fruit described—especially valuable to the novice. The fruit key (both deciduous trees and evergreens) has an introduction explaining seeding, organs involved, fruit types and habits. The twig key introduction treats growth and morphology. In the keys proper, identification is easy and almost automatic. This exceptional work, widely used in university courses, is especially useful for identification in winter, or from the fruit or seed only. Over 350 photos, up to 3 times natural size. Bibliography, glossary, index of common and scientific names, in each key. xvii + 125pp. 5⅝ x 8⅜.
T511 Paperbound **$1.25**

HOW TO KNOW THE FERNS, F. T. Parsons. Ferns, among our most lovely native plants, are all too little known. This modern classic of nature lore will enable the layman to identify any American fern he is likely to come across. After an introduction on the structure and life of ferns, the 57 most important ferns are fully pictured and described (arranged upon a simple identification key). Index of Latin and English names. 61 illustrations and 42 full-page plates. xiv + 215pp. 5⅜ x 8.
T740 Paperbound **$1.35**

OUR SMALL NATIVE ANIMALS: THEIR HABITS AND CARE, R. Snedigar, Curator of Reptiles, Chicago Zoological Park. An unusual nature handbook containing all the vital facts of habitat, distribution, foods, and special habits in brief life histories of 114 different species of squirrels, chipmunks, rodents, larger mammals, birds, amphibians, lizards and snakes. Liberally sprinkled with first-hand anecdotes. A wealth of information on capturing and caring for these animals: proper pens and cages, correct diet, curing diseases, special equipment required, etc. Addressed to the teacher interested in classroom demonstrations, the camp director, and to anyone who ever wanted a small animal for a pet. Revised edition, New preface. Index. 62 halftones. 14 line drawings. xviii + 296pp. 5⅜ x 8⅛.
T1022 Paperbound **$1.75**

INSECT LIFE AND INSECT NATURAL HISTORY, S. W. Frost. Unusual for emphasizing habits, social life, and ecological relations of insects, rather than more academic aspects of classification and morphology. Prof. Frost's enthusiasm and knowledge are everywhere evident as he discusses insect associations, and specialized habits like leaf-mining, leaf-rolling, and case-making, the gall insects, the boring insects, aquatic insects, etc. He examines all sorts of matters not usually covered in general works, such as: insects as human food; insect music and musicians; insect response to electric and radio waves; use of insects in art and literature. The admirably executed purpose of this book, which covers the middle ground between elementary treatment and scholarly monographs, is to excite the reader to observe for himself. Over 700 illustrations. Extensive bibliography. x + 524pp. 5⅜ x 8.
T517 Paperbound **$2.45**

Biological Sciences

AN INTRODUCTION TO GENETICS, A. H. Sturtevant and G. W. Beadle. A very thorough exposition of genetic analysis and the chromosome mechanics of higher organisms by two of the world's most renowned biologists, A. H. Sturtevant, one of the founders of modern genetics, and George Beadle, Nobel laureate in 1958. Does not concentrate on the biochemical approach, but rather more on observed data from experimental evidence and results . . . from Drosophila and other life forms. Some chapter titles: Sex chromosomes; Sex-Linkage; Autosomal Inheritance;; Chromosome Maps; Intra-Chromosomal Rearrangements; Inversions—and Incomplete Chromosomes; Translocations; Lethals; Mutations; Heterogeneous Populations; Genes and Phenotypes; The Determination and Differentiation of Sex; etc. Slightly corrected reprint of 1939 edition. New preface by Drs. Sturtevant and Beadle. 1 color plate. 126 figures. Bibliographies. Index. 391pp. 5⅜ x 8½. S306 Paperbound **$2.00**

THE GENETICAL THEORY OF NATURAL SELECTION, R. A. Fisher. 2nd revised edition of a vital reviewing of Darwin's Selection Theory in terms of particulate inheritance, by one of the great authorities on experimental and theoretical genetics. Theory is stated in mathematical form. Special features of particulate inheritance are examined: evolution of dominance, maintenance of specific variability, mimicry and sexual selection, etc. 5 chapters on man and his special circumstances as a social animal. 16 photographs. Bibliography. Index. x + 310pp. 5⅜ x 8. S466 Paperbound **$2.00**

THE ORIENTATION OF ANIMALS: KINESES, TAXES AND COMPASS REACTIONS, Gottfried S. Fraenkel and Donald L. Gunn. A basic work in the field of animal orientations. Complete, detailed survey of everything known in the subject up to 1940s, enlarged and revised to cover major developments to 1960. Analyses of simpler types of orientation are presented in Part I: kinesis, klinotaxis, tropotaxis, telotaxis, etc. Part II covers more complex reactions originating from temperature changes, gravity, chemical stimulation, etc. The two-light experiment and unilateral blinding are dealt with, as is the problem of determinism or volition in lower animals. The book has become the universally-accepted guide to all who deal with the subject—zoologists, biologists, psychologists, and the like. Second, enlarged edition, revised to 1960. Bibliography of over 500 items. 135 illustrations. Indices. xiii + 376pp. 5⅜ x 8½. T786 Paperbound **$2.25**

THE BEHAVIOUR AND SOCIAL LIFE OF HONEYBEES, C. R. Ribbands. Definitive survey of all aspects of honeybee life and behavior; completely scientific in approach, but written in interesting, everyday language that both professionals and laymen will appreciate. Basic coverage of physiology, anatomy, sensory equipment; thorough account of honeybee behavior in the field (foraging activities, nectar and pollen gathering, how individuals find their way home and back to food areas, mating habits, etc.); details of communication in various field and hive situations. An extensive treatment of activities within the hive community—food sharing, wax production, comb building, swarming, the queen, her life and relationship with the workers, etc. A must for the beekeeper, natural historian, biologist, entomologist, social scientist, et al. "An indispensable reference," J. Hambleton, BEES. "Recommended in the strongest of terms," AMERICAN SCIENTIST. 9 plates. 66 figures. Indices. 693-item bibliography. 252pp. 5⅜ x 8½. T1137 Paperbound **$2.00**

BIRD DISPLAY: AN INTRODUCTION TO THE STUDY OF BIRD PSYCHOLOGY, E. A. Armstrong. The standard work on bird display, based on extensive observation by the author and reports of other observers. This important contribution to comparative psychology covers the behavior and ceremonial rituals of hundreds of birds from gannet and heron to birds of paradise and king penguins. Chapters discuss such topics as the ceremonial of the gannet, ceremonial gaping, disablement reactions, the expression of emotions, the evolution and function of social ceremonies, social hierarchy in bird life, dances of birds and men, songs, etc. Free of technical terminology, this work will be equally interesting to psychologists and zoologists as well as bird lovers of all backgrounds. 32 photographic plates. New introduction by the author. List of scientific names of birds. Bibliography. 3-part index. 431pp. 5⅜ x 8½. T1128 Paperbound **$2.00**

THE SPECIFICITY OF SEROLOGICAL REACTIONS, Karl Landsteiner. With a Chapter on Molecular Structure and Intermolecular Forces by Linus Pauling. Dr. Landsteiner, winner of the Nobel Prize in 1930 for the discovery of the human blood groups, devoted his life to fundamental research and played a leading role in the development of immunology. This authoritative study is an account of the experiments he and his colleagues carried out on antigens and serological reactions with simple compounds. Comprehensive coverage of the basic concepts of immunolgy includes such topics as: The Serological Specificity of Proteins, Antigens, Antibodies, Artificially Conjugated Antigens, Non-Protein Cell Substances such as polysaccharides, etc., Antigen-Antibody Reactions (Toxin Neutralization, Precipitin Reactions, Agglutination, etc.). Discussions of toxins, bacterial proteins, viruses, hormones, enzymes, etc. in the context of immunological phenomena. New introduction by Dr. Merrill Chase of the Rockefeller Institute. Extensive bibliography and bibliography of author's writings. Index. xviii + 330pp. 5⅜ x 8½. S299 Paperbound **$2.00**

CULTURE METHODS FOR INVERTEBRATE ANIMALS, P. S. Galtsoff, F. E. Lutz, P. S. Welch, J. G. Needham, eds. A compendium of practical experience of hundreds of scientists and technicians, covering invertebrates from protozoa to chordata, in 313 articles on 17 phyla. Explains in great detail food, protection, environment, reproduction conditions, rearing methods, embryology, breeding seasons, schedule of development, much more. Includes at least one species of each considerable group. Half the articles are on class insecta. Introduction. 97 illustrations. Bibliography. Index. xxix + 590pp. 5⅜ x 8. S526 Paperbound **$3.00**

THE BIOLOGY OF THE LABORATORY MOUSE, edited by **G. D. Snell.** 1st prepared in 1941 by the staff of the Roscoe B. Jackson Memorial Laboratory, this is still the standard treatise on the mouse, assembling an enormous amount of material for which otherwise you spend hours of research. Embryology, reproduction, histology, spontaneous tumor formation, genetics of tumor transplantation, endocrine secretion & tumor formation, milk, influence & tumor formation, inbred, hybrid animals, parasites, infectious diseases, care & recording. Classified bibliography of 1122 items. 172 figures, including 128 photos. ix + 497pp. 6⅛ x 9¼. S248 Clothbound **$6.00**

MATHEMATICAL BIOPHYSICS: PHYSICO-MATHEMATICAL FOUNDATIONS OF BIOLOGY, N. Rashevsky. One of most important books in modern biology, now revised, expanded with new chapters, to include most significant recent contributions. Vol. 1: Diffusion phenomena, particularly diffusion drag forces, their effects. Old theory of cell division based on diffusion drag forces, other theoretical approaches, more exhaustively treated than ever. Theories of excitation, conduction in nerves, with formal theories plus physico-chemical theory. Vol. 2: Mathematical theories of various phenomena in central nervous system. New chapters on theory of color vision, of random nets. Principle of optimal design, extended from earlier edition. Principle of relational mapping of organisms, numerous applications. Introduces into mathematical biology such branches of math as topology, theory of sets. Index. 236 illustrations. Total of 988pp. 5⅜ x 8.
S574 Vol. 1 (Books 1, 2) Paperbound **$2.50**
S575 Vol. 2 (Books 3, 4) Paperbound **$2.50**
2 vol. set **$5.00**

ELEMENTS OF MATHEMATICAL BIOLOGY, A. J. Lotka. A pioneer classic, the first major attempt to apply modern mathematical techniques on a large scale to phenomena of biology, biochemistry, psychology, ecology, similar life sciences. Partial Contents: Statistical meaning of irreversibility; Evolution as redistribution; Equations of kinetics of evolving systems; Chemical, inter-species equilibrium; parameters of state; Energy transformers of nature, etc. Can be read with profit even by those having no advanced math; unsurpassed as study-reference. Formerly titled ELEMENTS OF PHYSICAL BIOLOGY. 72 figures. xxx + 460pp. 5⅜ x 8. S346 Paperbound **$2.45**

THE BIOLOGY OF THE AMPHIBIA, G. K. Noble, Late Curator of Herpetology at the Am. Mus. of Nat. Hist. Probably the most used text on amphibia, unmatched in comprehensiveness, clarity, detail. 19 chapters plus 85-page supplement cover development; heredity; life history; speciation; adaptation; sex, integument, respiratory, circulatory, digestive, muscular, nervous systems; instinct, intelligence, habits, environment, economic value, relationships, classification, etc. "Nothing comparable to it," C. H. Pope, Curator of Amphibia, Chicago Mus. of Nat. Hist. 1047 bibliographic references. 174 illustrations. 600pp. 5⅜ x 8. S206 Paperbound **$2.98**

STUDIES ON THE STRUCTURE AND DEVELOPMENT OF VERTEBRATES, E. S. Goodrich. A definitive study by the greatest modern comparative anatomist. Exceptional in its accounts of the ossicles of the ear, the separate divisions of the coelom and mammalian diaphragm, and the 5 chapters devoted to the head region. Also exhaustive morphological and phylogenetic expositions of skeleton, fins and limbs, skeletal visceral arches and labial cartilages, visceral clefts and gills, vacular, respiratory, excretory, and peripheral nervous systems, etc., from fish to the higher mammals. 754 illustrations. 69 page biographical study by C. C. Hardy. Bibliography of 1186 references. "What an undertaking . . . to write a textbook which will summarize adequately and succinctly all that has been done in the realm of Vertebrate Morphology these recent years," Journal of Anatomy. Index. Two volumes. Total 906pp. 5⅜ x 8. Two vol. set S449-50 Paperbound **$5.00**

A TREATISE ON PHYSIOLOGICAL OPTICS, H. von Helmholtz, Ed. by J. P. C. Southall. Unmatched for thoroughness, soundness, and comprehensiveness, this is still the most important work ever produced in the field of physiological optics. Revised and annotated, it contains everything known about the subject up to 1925. Beginning with a careful anatomical description of the eye, the main body of the text is divided into three general categories: The Dioptrics of the Eye (covering optical imagery, blur circles on the retina, the mechanism of accommodation, chromatic aberration, etc.); The Sensations of Vision (including stimulation of the organ of vision, simple and compound colors, the intensity and duration of light, variations of sensitivity, contrast, etc.); and The Perceptions of Vision (containing movements of the eyes, the monocular field of vision, direction, perception of depth, binocular double vision, etc.). Appendices cover later findings on optical imagery, refraction, ophthalmoscopy, and many other matters. Unabridged, corrected republication of the original English translation of the third German edition. 3 volumes bound as 2. Complete bibliography, 1911-1925. Indices. 312 illustrations. 6 full-page plates, 3 in color. Total of 1,749pp. 5⅜ x 8. Two-volume set S15, 16 Clothbound **$15.00**

INTRODUCTION TO PHYSIOLOGICAL OPTICS, James P. C. Southall, former Professor of Physics in Columbia University. Readable, top-flight introduction, not only for beginning students of optics, but also for other readers—physicists, biochemists, illuminating engineers, optometrists, psychologists, etc. Comprehensive coverage of such matters as the Organ of Vision (structure of the eyeball, the retina, the dioptric system, monocular and binocular vision, adaptation, etc.); The Optical System of the Eye (reflex images in the cornea and crystalline lens, Emmetropia and Ametropia, accommodation, blur circles on retina); Eye-Glasses; Eye Defects; Movements of the Eyeball in its Socket; Rod and Cone Vision; Color Vision; and other similar topics. Index. 134 figures. x +426pp. 5⅜ x 8. S924 Paperbound **$2.25**

LIGHT, COLOUR AND VISION, Yves LeGrand. A thorough examination of the eye as a receptor of radiant energy and as a mechanism (the retina) consisting of light-sensitive cells which absorb light of various wave lengths—probably the most complete and authoritative treatment of this subject in print. Originally prepared as a series of lectures given at the Institute of Optics in Paris, subsequently enlarged for book publication. Partial contents: Radiant Energy—concept, nature, theories, etc., Sources of Radiation—artificial and natural, the Visual Receptor, Photometric Quantities, Units, Calculations, Retinal Illumination, Trivariance of Vision, Colorimetry, Luminance Difference Thresholds, Anatomy of the Retina, Theories of Vision, Photochemistry and Electro-physiology of the Retina, etc. Appendices, Exercises, with solutions. 500-item bibliography. Authorized translation by R. Hunt, J. Walsh, F. Hunt. Index. 173 illustrations. xiii + 512pp. 5⅜ x 8½. S979 Clothbound **$10.00**

FINGER PRINTS, PALMS AND SOLES: AN INTRODUCTION TO DERMATOGLYPHICS, Harold Cummins and Charles Midlo. An introduction in non-technical language designed to acquaint the reader with a long-neglected aspect of human biology. Although a chapter dealing with fingerprint identification and the systems of classification used by the FBI, etc. has been added especially for this edition, the main concern of the book is to show how the intricate pattern of ridges and wrinkles on our fingers have a broader significance, applicable in many areas of science and life. Some topics are: the identification of two types of twins; the resolution of doubtful cases of paternity; racial variation; inheritance; the relation of fingerprints to body measurements, blood groups, criminality, character, etc. Classification and recognition of fundamental patterns and pattern types discussed fully. 149 figures. 49 tables. 361-item bibliography. Index. xii + 319pp. 5⅝ x 8⅜. T778 Paperbound **$1.95**

Classics and histories

ANTONY VAN LEEUWENHOEK AND HIS "LITTLE ANIMALS," edited by Clifford Dobell. First book to treat extensively, accurately, life and works (relating to protozoology, bacteriology) of first microbiologist, bacteriologist, micrologist. Includes founding papers of protozoology, bacteriology; history of Leeuwenhoek's life; discussions of his microscopes, methods, language. His writing conveys sense of an enthusiastic, naive genius, as he looks at rainwater, pepper water, vinegar, frog's skin, rotifers, etc. Extremely readable, even for non-specialists. "One of the most interesting and enlightening books I have ever read," Dr. C. C. Bass, former Dean, Tulane U. School of Medicine. Only authorized edition. 400-item bibliography. Index. 32 illust. 442pp. 5⅜ x 8. S594 Paperbound **$2.25**

THE GROWTH OF SCIENTIFIC PHYSIOLOGY, G. J. Goodfield. A compact, superbly written account of how certain scientific investigations brought about the emergence of the distinct science of physiology. Centers principally around the mechanist-vitalist controversy prior to the development of physiology as an independent science, using the arguments which raged around the problem of animal heat as its chief illustration. Covers thoroughly the efforts of clinicians and naturalists and workers in chemistry and physics to solve these problems—from which the new discipline arose. Includes the theories and contributions of: Aristotle, Galen, Harvey, Boyle, Bernard, Benjamin Franklin, Palmer, Gay-Lussac, Priestley, Spallanzani, and many others. 1960 publication. Biographical bibliography. 174pp. 5 x 7½. T1066 Clothbound **$3.00**

MICROGRAPHIA, Robert Hooke. Hooke, 17th century British universal scientific genius, was a major pioneer in celestial mechanics, optics, gravity, and many other fields, but his greatest contribution was this book, now reprinted entirely from the original 1665 edition, which gave microscopy its first great impetus. With all the freshness of discovery, he describes fully his microscope, and his observations of cork, the edge of a razor, insects' eyes, fabrics, and dozens of other different objects. 38 plates, full-size or larger, contain all the original illustrations. This book is also a fundamental classic in the fields of combustion and heat theory, light and color theory, botany and zoology, hygrometry, and many other fields. It contains such farsighted predictions as the famous anticipation of artificial silk. The final section is concerned with Hooke's telescopic observations of the moon and stars. 323pp. 5⅜ x 8. T8 Paperbound **$2.00**

(*) The more difficult books are indicated by an asterisk

Books Explaining Science and Mathematics

WHAT IS SCIENCE?, N. Campbell. The role of experiment and measurement, the function of mathematics, the nature of scientific laws, the difference between laws and theories, the limitations of science, and many similarly provocative topics are treated clearly and without technicalities by an eminent scientist. "Still an excellent introduction to scientific philosophy," H. Margenau in PHYSICS TODAY. "A first-rate primer . . . deserves a wide audience," SCIENTIFIC AMERICAN. 192pp. 5⅜ x 8. S43 Paperbound **$1.25**

THE NATURE OF PHYSICAL THEORY, P. W. Bridgman. A Nobel Laureate's clear, non-technical lectures on difficulties and paradoxes connected with frontier research on the physical sciences. Concerned with such central concepts as thought, logic, mathematics, relativity, probability, wave mechanics, etc. he analyzes the contributions of such men as Newton, Einstein, Bohr, Heisenberg, and many others. "Lucid and entertaining . . . recommended to anyone who wants to get some insight into current philosophies of science," THE NEW PHILOSOPHY. Index. xi + 138pp. 5⅜ x 8. S33 Paperbound **$1.25**

EXPERIMENT AND THEORY IN PHYSICS, Max Born. A Nobel Laureate examines the nature of experiment and theory in theoretical physics and analyzes the advances made by the great physicists of our day: Heisenberg, Einstein, Bohr, Planck, Dirac, and others. The actual process of creation is detailed step-by-step by one who participated. A fine examination of the scientific method at work. 44pp. 5⅜ x 8. S308 Paperbound **75¢**

THE PSYCHOLOGY OF INVENTION IN THE MATHEMATICAL FIELD, J. Hadamard. The reports of such men as Descartes, Pascal, Einstein, Poincaré, and others are considered in this investigation of the method of idea-creation in mathematics and other sciences and the thinking process in general. How do ideas originate? What is the role of the unconscious? What is Poincaré's forgetting hypothesis? are some of the fascinating questions treated. A penetrating analysis of Einstein's thought processes concludes the book. xiii + 145pp. 5⅜ x 8. T107 Paperbound **$1.25**

THE NATURE OF LIGHT AND COLOUR IN THE OPEN AIR, M. Minnaert. Why are shadows sometimes blue, sometimes green, or other colors depending on the light and surroundings? What causes mirages? Why do multiple suns and moons appear in the sky? Professor Minnaert explains these unusual phenomena and hundreds of others in simple, easy-to-understand terms based on optical laws and the properties of light and color. No mathematics is required but artists, scientists, students, and everyone fascinated by these "tricks" of nature will find thousands of useful and amazing pieces of information. Hundreds of observational experiments are suggested which require no special equipment. 200 illustrations; 42 photos. xvi + 362pp. 5⅜ x 8. T196 Paperbound **$2.00**

***MATHEMATICS IN ACTION, O. G. Sutton.** Everyone with a command of high school algebra will find this book one of the finest possible introductions to the application of mathematics to physical theory. Ballistics, numerical analysis, waves and wavelike phenomena, Fourier series, group concepts, fluid flow and aerodynamics, statistical measures, and meteorology are discussed with unusual clarity. Some calculus and differential equations theory is developed by the author for the reader's help in the more difficult sections. 88 figures. Index. viii + 236pp. 5⅜ x 8. T440 Clothbound **$3.50**

SOAP-BUBBLES: THEIR COLOURS AND THE FORCES THAT MOULD THEM, C. V. Boys. For continuing popularity and validity as scientific primer, few books can match this volume of easily-followed experiments, explanations. Lucid exposition of complexities of liquid films, surface tension and related phenomena, bubbles' reaction to heat, motion, music, magnetic fields. Experiments with capillary attraction, soap bubbles on frames, composite bubbles, liquid cylinders and jets, bubbles other than soap, etc. Wonderful introduction to scientific method, natural laws that have many ramifications in areas of modern physics. Only complete edition in print. New Introduction by S. Z. Lewin, New York University. 83 illustrations; 1 full-page color plate. xii + 190pp. 5⅜ x 8½. T542 Paperbound **95¢**

THE STORY OF X-RAYS FROM RÖNTGEN TO ISOTOPES, A. R. Bleich, M.D. This book, by a member of the American College of Radiology, gives the scientific explanation of x-rays, their applications in medicine, industry and art, and their danger (and that of atmospheric radiation) to the individual and the species. You learn how radiation therapy is applied against cancer, how x-rays diagnose heart disease and other ailments, how they are used to examine mummies for information on diseases of early societies, and industrial materials for hidden weaknesses. 54 illustrations show x-rays of flowers, bones, stomach, gears with flaws, etc. 1st publication. Index. xix + 186pp. 5⅜ x 8. T622 Paperbound **$1.35**

SPINNING TOPS AND GYROSCOPIC MOTION, John Perry. A classic elementary text of the dynamics of rotation — the behavior and use of rotating bodies such as gyroscopes and tops. In simple, everyday English you are shown how quasi-rigidity is induced in discs of paper, smoke rings, chains, etc., by rapid motions; why a gyrostat falls and why a top rises; precession; how the earth's motion affects climate; and many other phenomena. Appendix on practical use of gyroscopes. 62 figures. 128pp. 5⅜ x 8. T416 Paperbound **$1.00**

SNOW CRYSTALS, W. A. Bentley, M. J. Humphreys. For almost 50 years W. A. Bentley photographed snow flakes in his laboratory in Jericho, Vermont; in 1931 the American Meteorological Society gathered together the best of his work, some 2400 photographs of snow flakes, plus a few ice flowers, windowpane frosts, dew, frozen rain, and other ice formations. Pictures were selected for beauty and scientific value. A very valuable work to anyone in meteorology, cryology; most interesting to layman; extremely useful for artist who wants beautiful, crystalline designs. All copyright free. Unabridged reprint of 1931 edition. 2453 illustrations. 227pp. 8 x 10½. T287 Paperbound **$3.00**

A DOVER SCIENCE SAMPLER, edited by George Barkin. A collection of brief, non-technical passages from 44 Dover Books Explaining Science for the enjoyment of the science-minded browser. Includes work of Bertrand Russell, Poincaré, Laplace, Max Born, Galileo, Newton; material on physics, mathematics, metallurgy, anatomy, astronomy, chemistry, etc. You will be fascinated by Martin Gardner's analysis of the sincere pseudo-scientist, Moritz's account of Newton's absentmindedness, Bernard's examples of human vivisection, etc. Illustrations from the Diderot Pictorial Encyclopedia and De Re Metallica. 64 pages. **FREE**

THE STORY OF ATOMIC THEORY AND ATOMIC ENERGY, J. G. Feinberg. A broader approach to subject of nuclear energy and its cultural implications than any other similar source. Very readable, informal, completely non-technical text. Begins with first atomic theory, 600 B.C. and carries you through the work of Mendelejeff, Röntgen, Madame Curie, to Einstein's equation and the A-bomb. New chapter goes through thermonuclear fission, binding energy, other events up to 1959. Radioactive decay and radiation hazards, future benefits, work of Bohr, moderns, hundreds more topics. "Deserves special mention . . . not only authoritative but thoroughly popular in the best sense of the word," Saturday Review. Formerly, "The Atom Story." Expanded with new chapter. Three appendixes. Index. 34 illustrations. vii + 243pp. 5⅜ x 8. T625 Paperbound **$1.60**

THE STRANGE STORY OF THE QUANTUM, AN ACCOUNT FOR THE GENERAL READER OF THE GROWTH OF IDEAS UNDERLYING OUR PRESENT ATOMIC KNOWLEDGE, B. Hoffmann. Presents lucidly and expertly, with barest amount of mathematics, the problems and theories which led to modern quantum physics. Dr. Hoffmann begins with the closing years of the 19th century, when certain trifling discrepancies were noticed, and with illuminating analogies and examples takes you through the brilliant concepts of Planck, Einstein, Pauli, Broglie, Bohr, Schroedinger, Heisenberg, Dirac, Sommerfeld, Feynman, etc. This edition includes a new, long postscript carrying the story through 1958. "Of the books attempting an account of the history and contents of our modern atomic physics which have come to my attention, this is the best," H. Margenau, Yale University, in "American Journal of Physics." 32 tables and line illustrations. Index. 275pp. 5⅜ x 8. T518 Paperbound **$1.50**

SPACE AND TIME, E. Borel. Written by a versatile mathematician of world renown with his customary lucidity and precision, this introduction to relativity for the layman presents scores of examples, analogies, and illustrations that open up new ways of thinking about space and time. It covers abstract geometry and geographical maps, continuity and topology, the propagation of light, the special theory of relativity, the general theory of relativity, theoretical researches, and much more. Mathematical notes. 2 Indexes. 4 Appendices. 15 figures. xvi + 243pp. 5⅜ x 8. T592 Paperbound **$1.45**

FROM EUCLID TO EDDINGTON: A STUDY OF THE CONCEPTIONS OF THE EXTERNAL WORLD, Sir Edmund Whittaker. A foremost British scientist traces the development of theories of natural philosophy from the western rediscovery of Euclid to Eddington, Einstein, Dirac, etc. The inadequacy of classical physics is contrasted with present day attempts to understand the physical world through relativity, non-Euclidean geometry, space curvature, wave mechanics, etc. 5 major divisions of examination: Space; Time and Movement; the Concepts of Classical Physics; the Concepts of Quantum Mechanics; the Eddington Universe. 212pp. 5⅜ x 8. T491 Paperbound **$1.35**

***THE EVOLUTION OF SCIENTIFIC THOUGHT FROM NEWTON TO EINSTEIN, A. d'Abro.** A detailed account of the evolution of classical physics into modern relativistic theory and the concommitant changes in scientific methodology. The breakdown of classical physics in the face of non-Euclidean geometry and the electromagnetic equations is carefully discussed and then an exhaustive analysis of Einstein's special and general theories of relativity and their implications is given. Newton, Riemann, Weyl, Lorentz, Planck, Maxwell, and many others are considered. A non-technical explanation of space, time, electromagnetic waves, etc. as understood today. "Model of semi-popular exposition," NEW REPUBLIC. 21 diagrams. 482pp. 5⅜ x 8.
T2 Paperbound **$2.25**

EINSTEIN'S THEORY OF RELATIVITY, Max Born. Nobel Laureate explains Einstein's special and general theories of relativity, beginning with a thorough review of classical physics in simple, non-technical language. Exposition of Einstein's work discusses concept of simultaneity, kinematics, relativity of arbitrary motions, the space-time continuum, geometry of curved surfaces, etc., steering middle course between vague popularizations and complex scientific presentations. 1962 edition revised by author takes into account latest findings, predictions of theory and implications for cosmology, indicates what is being sought in unified field theory. Mathematics very elementary, illustrative diagrams and experiments informative but simple. Revised 1962 edition. Revised by Max Born, assisted by Gunther Leibfried and Walter Biem. Index. 143 illustrations. vii + 376pp. 5⅜ x 8.
S769 Paperbound **$2.00**

PHILOSOPHY AND THE PHYSICISTS, L. Susan Stebbing. A philosopher examines the philosophical aspects of modern science, in terms of a lively critical attack on the ideas of Jeans and Eddington. Such basic questions are treated as the task of science, causality, determinism, probability, consciousness, the relation of the world of physics to the world of everyday experience. The author probes the concepts of man's smallness before an inscrutable universe, the tendency to idealize mathematical construction, unpredictability theorems and human freedom, the supposed opposition between 19th century determinism and modern science, and many others. Introduces many thought-stimulating ideas about the implications of modern physical concepts. xvi + 295pp. 5⅜ x 8. T480 Paperbound **$1.65**

THE RESTLESS UNIVERSE, Max Born. A remarkably lucid account by a Nobel Laureate of recent theories of wave mechanics, behavior of gases, electrons and ions, waves and particles, electronic structure of the atom, nuclear physics, and similar topics. "Much more thorough and deeper than most attempts . . . easy and delightful," CHEMICAL AND ENGINEERING NEWS. Special feature: 7 animated sequences of 60 figures each showing such phenomena as gas molecules in motion, the scattering of alpha particles, etc. 11 full-page plates of photographs. Total of nearly 600 illustrations. 351pp. 6⅛ x 9¼. T412 Paperbound **$2.00**

THE COMMON SENSE OF THE EXACT SCIENCES, W. K. Clifford. For 70 years a guide to the basic concepts of scientific and mathematical thought. Acclaimed by scientists and laymen alike, it offers a wonderful insight into concepts such as the extension of meaning of symbols, characteristics of surface boundaries, properties of plane figures, measurement of quantities, vectors, the nature of position, bending of space, motion, mass and force, and many others. Prefaces by Bertrand Russell and Karl Pearson. Critical introduction by James Newman. 130 figures. 249pp. 5⅜ x 8. T61 Paperbound **$1.60**

MATTER AND LIGHT, THE NEW PHYSICS, Louis de Broglie. Non-technical explanations by a Nobel Laureate of electro-magnetic theory, relativity, matter, light and radiation, wave mechanics, quantum physics, philosophy of science, and similar topics. This is one of the simplest yet most accurate introductions to the work of men like Planck, Einstein, Bohr, and others. Only 2 of the 21 chapters require a knowledge of mathematics. 300pp. 5⅜ x 8.
T35 Paperbound **$1.85**

SCIENCE, THEORY AND MAN, Erwin Schrödinger. This is a complete and unabridged reissue of SCIENCE AND THE HUMAN TEMPERAMENT plus an additional essay: "What Is an Elementary Particle?" Nobel Laureate Schrödinger discusses such topics as nature of scientific method, tne nature of science, chance and determinism, science and society, conceptual models for physical entities, elementary particles and wave mechanics. Presentation is popular and may be followed by most people with little or no scientific training. "Fine practical preparation for a time when laws of nature, human institutions . . . are undergoing a critical examination without parallel," Waldemar Kaempffert, N. Y. TIMES. 192pp. 5⅜ x 8.
T428 Paperbound **$1.35**

CONCERNING THE NATURE OF THINGS, Sir William Bragg. The Nobel Laureate physicist in his Royal Institute Christmas Lectures explains such diverse phenomena as the formation of crystals, how uranium is transmuted to lead, the way X-rays work, why a spinning ball travels in a curved path, the reason why bubbles bounce from each other, and many other scientific topics that are seldom explained in simple terms. No scientific background needed—book is easy enough that any intelligent adult or youngster can understand it. Unabridged. 32pp. of photos; 57 figures. xii + 232pp. 5⅜ x 8. T31 Paperbound **$1.35**

***THE RISE OF THE NEW PHYSICS (formerly THE DECLINE OF MECHANISM), A. d'Abro.** This authoritative and comprehensive 2 volume exposition is unique in scientific publishing. Written for intelligent readers not familiar with higher mathematics, it is the only thorough explanation in non-technical language of modern mathematical-physical theory. Combining both history and exposition, it ranges from classical Newtonian concepts up through the electronic theories of Dirac and Heisenberg, the statistical mechanics of Fermi, and Einstein's relativity theories. "A must for anyone doing serious study in the physical sciences," J. OF FRANKLIN INST. 97 illustrations. 991pp. 2 volumes. T3 Vol. 1, Paperbound **$2.25**
T4 Vol. 2, Paperbound **$2.25**

CATALOGUE OF DOVER BOOKS

SCIENCE AND HYPOTHESIS, Henri Poincaré. Creative psychology in science. How such concepts as number, magnitude, space, force, classical mechanics were developed and how the modern scientist uses them in his thought. Hypothesis in physics, theories of modern physics. Introduction by Sir James Larmor. "Few mathematicians have had the breadth of vision of Poincaré, and none is his superior in the gift of clear exposition," E. T. Bell. Index. 272pp. 5⅜ x 8.
S221 Paperbound **$1.35**

THE VALUE OF SCIENCE, Henri Poincaré. Many of the most mature ideas of the "last scientific universalist" conveyed with charm and vigor for both the beginning student and the advanced worker. Discusses the nature of scientific truth, whether order is innate in the universe or imposed upon it by man, logical thought versus intuition (relating to mathematics through the works of Weierstrass, Lie, Klein, Riemann), time and space (relativity, psychological time, simultaneity), Hertz's concept of force, interrelationship of mathematical physics to pure math, values within disciplines of Maxwell, Carnot, Mayer, Newton, Lorentz, etc. Index. iii + 147pp. 5⅜ x 8. S469 Paperbound **$1.35**

THE SKY AND ITS MYSTERIES, E. A. Beet. One of the most lucid books on the mysteries of the universe; covers history of astronomy from earliest observations to modern theories of expanding universe, source of stellar energy, birth of planets, origin of moon craters, possibilities of life on other planets. Discusses effects of sunspots on weather; distance, age of stars; methods and tools of astronomers; much more. Expert and fascinating. "Eminently readable book," London Times. Bibliography. Over 50 diagrams, 12 full-page plates. Fold-out star map. Introduction. Index. 238pp. 5¼ x 7½. T627 Clothbound **$3.50**

OUT OF THE SKY: AN INTRODUCTION TO METEORITICS, H. H. Nininger. A non-technical yet comprehensive introduction to the young science of meteoritics: all aspects of the arrival of cosmic matter on our planet from outer space and the reaction and alteration of this matter in the terrestrial environment. Essential facts and major theories presented by one of the world's leading experts. Covers ancient reports of meteors; modern systematic investigations; fireball clusters; meteorite showers; tektites; planetoidal encounters; etc. 52 full-page plates with over 175 photographs. 22 figures. Bibliography and references. Index. viii + 336pp. 5⅜ x 8.
T519 Paperbound **$1.85**

THE REALM OF THE NEBULAE, E. Hubble. One of great astronomers of our day records his formulation of concept of "island universes." Covers velocity-distance relationship; classification, nature, distances, general types of nebulae; cosmological theories. A fine introduction to modern theories for layman. No math needed. New introduction by A. Sandage. 55 illustrations, photos. Index. iv + 201pp. 5⅜ x 8. S455 Paperbound **$1.50**

AN ELEMENTARY SURVEY OF CELESTIAL MECHANICS, Y. Ryabov. Elementary exposition of gravitational theory and celestial mechanics. Historical introduction and coverage of basic principles, including: the ecliptic, the orbital plane, the 2- and 3-body problems, the discovery of Neptune, planetary rotation, the length of the day, the shapes of galaxies, satellites (detailed treatment of Sputnik I), etc. First American reprinting of successful Russian popular exposition. Follow actual methods of astrophysicists with only high school math! Appendix. 58 figures. 165pp. 5⅜ x 8. T756 Paperbound **$1.25**

GREAT IDEAS AND THEORIES OF MODERN COSMOLOGY, Jagjit Singh. Companion volume to author's popular "Great Ideas of Modern Mathematics" (Dover, $1.55). The best non-technical survey of post-Einstein attempts to answer perhaps unanswerable questions of origin, age of Universe, possibility of life on other worlds, etc. Fundamental theories of cosmology and cosmogony recounted, explained, evaluated in light of most recent data: Einstein's concepts of relativity, space-time; Milne's a priori world-system; astrophysical theories of Jeans, Eddington; Hoyle's "continuous creation;" contributions of dozens more scientists. A faithful, comprehensive critical summary of complex material presented in an extremely well-written text intended for laymen. Original publication. Index. xii + 276pp. 5⅜ x 8½. T925 Paperbound **$1.85**

BASIC ELECTRICITY, Bureau of Naval Personnel. Very thorough, easily followed course in basic electricity for beginner, layman, or intermediate student. Begins with simplest definitions, presents coordinated, systematic coverage of basic theory and application: conductors, insulators, static electricity, magnetism, production of voltage, Ohm's law, direct current series and parallel circuits, wiring techniques, electromagnetism, alternating current, capacitance and inductance, measuring instruments, etc.; application to electrical machines such as alternating and direct current generators, motors, transformers, magnetic magnifiers, etc. Each chapter contains problems to test progress; answers at rear. No math needed beyond algebra. Appendices on signs, formulas, etc. 345 illustrations. 448pp. 7½ x 10.
S973 Paperbound **$3.00**

ELEMENTARY METALLURGY AND METALLOGRAPHY, A. M. Shrager. An introduction to common metals and alloys; stress is upon steel and iron, but other metals and alloys also covered. All aspects of production, processing, working of metals. Designed for student who wishes to enter metallurgy, for bright high school or college beginner, layman who wants background on extremely important industry. Questions, at ends of chapters, many microphotographs, glossary. Greatly revised 1961 edition. 195 illustrations, tables. ix + 389pp. 5⅜ x 8.
S138 Paperbound **$2.25**

BRIDGES AND THEIR BUILDERS, D. B. Steinman & S. R. Watson. Engineers, historians, and every person who has ever been fascinated by great spans will find this book an endless source of information and interest. Greek and Roman structures, Medieval bridges, modern classics such as the Brooklyn Bridge, and the latest developments in the science are retold by one of the world's leading authorities on bridge design and construction. BRIDGES AND THEIR BUILDERS is the only comprehensive and accurate semi-popular history of these important measures of progress in print. New, greatly revised, enlarged edition. 23 photos; 26 line-drawings. Index. xvii + 401pp. 5⅜ x 8. T431 Paperbound **$2.00**

FAMOUS BRIDGES OF THE WORLD, D. B. Steinman. An up-to-the-minute new edition of a book that explains the fascinating drama of how the world's great bridges came to be built. The author, designer of the famed Mackinac bridge, discusses bridges from all periods and all parts of the world, explaining their various types of construction, and describing the problems their builders faced. Although primarily for youngsters, this cannot fail to interest readers of all ages. 48 illustrations in the text. 23 photographs. 99pp. 6⅛ x 9¼. T161 Paperbound **$1.00**

HOW DO YOU USE A SLIDE RULE? by A. A. Merrill. A step-by-step explanation of the slide rule that presents the fundamental rules clearly enough for the non-mathematician to understand. Unlike most instruction manuals, this work concentrates on the two most important operations: multiplication and division. 10 easy lessons, each with a clear drawing, for the reader who has difficulty following other expositions. 1st publication. Index. 2 Appendices. 10 illustrations. 78 problems, all with answers. vi + 36 pp. 6⅛ x 9¼. T62 Paperbound **60¢**

HOW TO CALCULATE QUICKLY, H. Sticker. A tried and true method for increasing your "number sense" — the ability to see relationships between numbers and groups of numbers. Addition, subtraction, multiplication, division, fractions, and other topics are treated through techniques not generally taught in schools: left to right multiplication, division by inspection, etc. This is not a collection of tricks which work only on special numbers, but a detailed well-planned course, consisting of over 9,000 problems that you can work in spare moments. It is excellent for anyone who is inconvenienced by slow computational skills. 5 or 10 minutes of this book daily will double or triple your calculation speed. 9,000 problems, answers. 256pp. 5⅜ x 8. T295 Paperbound **$1.00**

MATHEMATICAL FUN, GAMES AND PUZZLES, Jack Frohlichstein. A valuable service for parents of children who have trouble with math, for teachers in need of a supplement to regular upper elementary and junior high math texts (each section is graded—easy, average, difficult —for ready adaptation to different levels of ability), and for just anyone who would like to develop basic skills in an informal and entertaining manner. The author combines ten years of experience as a junior high school math teacher with a method that uses puzzles and games to introduce the basic ideas and operations of arithmetic. Stress on everyday uses of math: banking, stock market, personal budgets, insurance, taxes. Intellectually stimulating and practical, too. 418 problems and diversions with answers. Bibliography. 120 illustrations. xix + 306pp. 5⅝ x 8½. T789 Paperbound **$1.75**

GREAT IDEAS OF MODERN MATHEMATICS: THEIR NATURE AND USE, Jagjit Singh. Reader with only high school math will understand main mathematical ideas of modern physics, astronomy, genetics, psychology, evolution, etc. better than many who use them as tools, but comprehend little of their basic structure. Author uses his wide knowledge of non-mathematical fields in brilliant exposition of differential equations, matrices, group theory, logic, statistics, problems of mathematical foundations, imaginary numbers, vectors, etc. Original publication. 2 appendixes. 2 indexes. 65 illustr. 322pp. 5⅜ x 8. S587 Paperbound **$1.75**

THE UNIVERSE OF LIGHT, W. Bragg. Sir William Bragg, Nobel Laureate and great modern physicist, is also well known for his powers of clear exposition. Here he analyzes all aspects of light for the layman: lenses, reflection, refraction, the optics of vision, x-rays, the photoelectric effect, etc. He tells you what causes the color of spectra, rainbows, and soap bubbles, how magic mirrors work, and much more. Dozens of simple experiments are described. Preface. Index. 199 line drawings and photographs, including 2 full-page color plates. x + 283pp. 5⅜ x 8. T538 Paperbound **$1.85**

***INTRODUCTION TO SYMBOLIC LOGIC AND ITS APPLICATIONS, Rudolph Carnap.** One of the clearest, most comprehensive, and rigorous introductions to modern symbolic logic, by perhaps its greatest living master. Not merely elementary theory, but demonstrated applications in mathematics, physics, and biology. Symbolic languages of various degrees of complexity are analyzed, and one constructed. "A creation of the rank of a masterpiece," Zentralblatt für Mathematik und Ihre Grenzgebiete. Over 300 exercises. 5 figures. Bibliography. Index. xvi + 241pp. 5⅜ x 8. S453 Paperbound **$1.85**

***HIGHER MATHEMATICS FOR STUDENTS OF CHEMISTRY AND PHYSICS, J. W. Mellor.** Not abstract, but practical, drawing its problems from familiar laboratory material, this book covers theory and application of differential calculus, analytic geometry, functions with singularities, integral calculus, infinite series, solution of numerical equations, differential equations, Fourier's theorem and extensions, probability and the theory of errors, calculus of variations, determinants, etc. "If the reader is not familiar with this book, it will repay him to examine it," CHEM. & ENGINEERING NEWS. 800 problems. 189 figures. 2 appendices; 30 tables of integrals, probability functions, etc. Bibliography. xxi + 641pp. 5⅜ x 8. S193 Paperbound **$2.50**

THE FOURTH DIMENSION SIMPLY EXPLAINED, edited by Henry P. Manning. Originally written as entries in contest sponsored by "Scientific American," then published in book form, these 22 essays present easily understood explanations of how the fourth dimension may be studied, the relationship of non-Euclidean geometry to the fourth dimension, analogies to three-dimensional space, some fourth-dimensional absurdities and curiosities, possible measurements and forms in the fourth dimension. In general, a thorough coverage of many of the simpler properties of fourth-dimensional space. Multi-points of view on many of the most important aspects are valuable aid to comprehension. Introduction by Dr. Henry P. Manning gives proper emphasis to points in essays, more advanced account of fourth-dimensional geometry. 82 figures. 251pp. 5⅜ x 8. T711 Paperbound **$1.35**

TRIGONOMETRY REFRESHER FOR TECHNICAL MEN, A. A. Klaf. A modern question and answer text on plane and spherical trigonometry. Part I covers plane trigonometry: angles, quadrants, trigonometrical functions, graphical representation, interpolation, equations, logarithms, solution of triangles, slide rules, etc. Part II discusses applications to navigation, surveying, elasticity, architecture, and engineering. Small angles, periodic functions, vectors, polar coordinates, De Moivre's theorem, fully covered. Part III is devoted to spherical trigonometry and the solution of spherical triangles, with applications to terrestrial and astronomical problems. Special time-savers for numerical calculation. 913 questions answered for you! 1738 problems; answers to odd numbers. 494 figures. 14 pages of functions, formulae. Index. x + 629pp. 5⅜ x 8. T371 Paperbound **$2.00**

CALCULUS REFRESHER FOR TECHNICAL MEN. A. A. Klaf. Not an ordinary textbook but a unique refresher for engineers, technicians, and students. An examination of the most important aspects of differential and integral calculus by means of 756 key questions. Part I covers simple differential calculus: constants, variables, functions, increments, derivatives, logarithms, curvature, etc. Part II treats fundamental concepts of integration: inspection, substitution, transformation, reduction, areas and volumes, mean value, successive and partial integration, double and triple integration. Stresses practical aspects! A 50 page section gives applications to civil and nautical engineering, electricity, stress and strain, elasticity, industrial engineering, and similar fields. 756 questions answered. 556 problems; solutions to odd numbers. 36 pages of constants, formulae. Index. v + 431pp. 5⅜ x 8.
T370 Paperbound **$2.00**

PROBABILITIES AND LIFE, Emile Borel. One of the leading French mathematicians of the last 100 years makes use of certain results of mathematics of probabilities and explains a number of problems that for the most part, are related to everyday living or to illness and death: computation of life expectancy tables, chances of recovery from various diseases, probabilities of job accidents, weather predictions, games of chance, and so on. Emphasis on results not processes, though some indication is made of mathematical proofs. Simple in style, free of technical terminology, limited in scope to everyday situations, it is comprehensible to laymen, fine reading for beginning students of probability. New English translation. Index. Appendix. vi + 87pp. 5⅜ x 8½. T121 Paperbound **$1.00**

POPULAR SCIENTIFIC LECTURES, Hermann von Helmholtz. 7 lucid expositions by a preeminent scientific mind: "The Physiological Causes of Harmony in Music," "On the Relation of Optics to Painting," "On the Conservation of Force," "On the Interaction of Natural Forces," "On Goethe's Scientific Researches" into theory of color, "On the Origin and Significance of Geometric Axioms," "On Recent Progress in the Theory of Vision." Written with simplicity of expression, stripped of technicalities, these are easy to understand and delightful reading for anyone interested in science or looking for an introduction to serious study of acoustics or optics. Introduction by Professor Morris Kline, Director, Division of Electromagnetic Research, New York University, contains astute, impartial evaluations. Selected from "Popular Lectures on Scientific Subjects," 1st and 2nd series. xii + 286pp. 5⅜ x 8½.
T799 Paperbound **$1.45**

SCIENCE AND METHOD, Henri Poincaré. Procedure of scientific discovery, methodology, experiment, idea-germination—the intellectual processes by which discoveries come into being. Most significant and most interesting aspects of development, application of ideas. Chapters cover selection of facts, chance, mathematical reasoning, mathematics, and logic; Whitehead, Russell, Cantor; the new mechanics, etc. 288pp. 5⅜ x 8. S222 Paperbound **$1.50**

HEAT AND ITS WORKINGS, Morton Mott-Smith, Ph.D. An unusual book; to our knowledge the only middle-level survey of this important area of science. Explains clearly such important concepts as physiological sensation of heat and Weber's law, measurement of heat, evolution of thermometer, nature of heat, expansion and contraction of solids, Boyle's law, specific heat. BTU's and calories, evaporation, Andrews's isothermals, radiation, the relation of heat to light, many more topics inseparable from other aspects of physics. A wide, non-mathematical yet thorough explanation of basic ideas, theories, phenomena for laymen and beginning scientists illustrated by experiences of daily life. Bibliography. 50 illustrations. x + 165pp. 5⅜ x 8½.
T978 Paperbound **$1.00**

New Books

101 PATCHWORK PATTERNS, Ruby Short McKim. With no more ability than the fundamentals of ordinary sewing, you will learn to make over 100 beautiful quilts: flowers, rainbows, Irish chains, fish and bird designs, leaf designs, unusual geometric patterns, many others. Cutting designs carefully diagrammed and described, suggestions for materials, yardage estimates, step-by-step instructions, plus entertaining stories of origins of quilt names, other folklore. Revised 1962. 101 full-sized patterns. 140 illustrations. Index. 128pp. 7⅞ x 10¾.
T773 Paperbound **$1.85**

ESSENTIAL GRAMMAR SERIES
By concentrating on the essential core of material that constitutes the semantically most important forms and areas of a language and by stressing explanation (often bringing parallel English forms into the discussion) rather than rote memory, this new series of grammar books is among the handiest language aids ever devised. Designed by linguists and teachers for adults with limited learning objectives and learning time, these books omit nothing important, yet they teach more usable language material and do it more quickly and permanently than any other self-study material. Clear and rigidly economical, they concentrate upon immediately usable language material, logically organized so that related material is always presented together. Any reader of typical capability can use them to refresh his grasp of language, to supplement self-study language records or conventional grammars used in schools, or to begin language study on his own. Now available:

ESSENTIAL GERMAN GRAMMAR, Dr. Guy Stern & E. F. Bleiler. Index. Glossary of terms. 128pp. 5⅜ x 8.
T422 Paperbound **$1.00**

ESSENTIAL FRENCH GRAMMAR, Dr. Seymour Resnick. Index. Cognate list. Glossary. 159pp. 5⅜ x 8.
T419 Paperbound **$1.00**

ESSENTIAL ITALIAN GRAMMAR, Dr. Olga Ragusa. Index. Glossary. 111pp. 5⅜ x 8.
T779 Paperbound **$1.00**

ESSENTIAL SPANISH GRAMMAR, Dr. Seymour Resnick. Index. 50-page cognate list. Glossary. 138pp. 5⅜ x 8.
T780 Paperbound **$1.00**

PHILOSOPHIES OF MUSIC HISTORY: A Study of General Histories of Music, 1600-1960, Warren D. Allen. Unquestionably one of the most significant documents yet to appear in musicology, this thorough survey covers the entire field of historical research in music. An influential masterpiece of scholarship, it includes early music histories; theories on the ethos of music; lexicons, dictionaries and encyclopedias of music; musical historiography through the centuries; philosophies of music history; scores of related topics. Copiously documented. New preface brings work up to 1960. Index. 317-item bibliography. 9 illustrations; 3 full-page plates. 5⅜ x 8½. xxxiv + 382pp.
T282 Paperbound **$2.00**

MR. DOOLEY ON IVRYTHING AND IVRYBODY, Finley Peter Dunne. The largest collection in print of hilarious utterances by the irrepressible Irishman of Archey Street, one of the most vital characters in American fiction. Gathered from the half dozen books that appeared during the height of Mr. Dooley's popularity, these 102 pieces are all unaltered and uncut, and they are all remarkably fresh and pertinent even today. Selected and edited by Robert Hutchinson. 5⅜ x 8½. xii + 244p.
T626 Paperbound **$1.00**

TREATISE ON PHYSIOLOGICAL OPTICS, Hermann von Helmholtz. Despite new investigations, this important work will probably remain preeminent. Contains everything known about physiological optics up to 1925, covering scores of topics under the general headings of dioptrics of the eye, sensations of vision, and perecptions of vision. Von Helmholtz's voluminous data are all included, as are extensive supplementary matter incorporated into the third German edition, new material prepared for 1925 English edition, and copious textual annotations by J. P. C. Southall. The most exhaustive treatise ever prepared on the subject, it has behind it a list of contributors that will never again be duplicated. Translated and edited by J. P. C. Southall. Bibliography. Indexes. 312 illustrations. 3 volumes bound as 2. Total of 1749pp. 5⅜ x 8.
S15-16 Two volume set, Clothbound **$15.00**

THE ARTISTIC ANATOMY OF TREES, Rex Vicat Cole. Even the novice with but an elementary knowledge of drawing and none of the structure of trees can learn to draw, paint trees from this systematic, lucid instruction book. Copiously illustrated with the author's own sketches, diagrams, and 50 paintings from the early Renaissance to today, it covers composition; structure of twigs, boughs, buds, branch systems; outline forms of major species; how leaf is set on twig; flowers and fruit and their arrangement; etc. 500 illustrations. Bibliography. Indexes. 347pp. 5⅜ x 8.
T1016 Clothbound **$4.50**

HOW PLANTS GET THEIR NAMES, L. H. Bailey. In this basic introduction to botanical nomenclature, a famed expert on plants and plant life reveals the confusion that can result from misleading common names of plants and points out the fun and advantage of using a sound, scientific approach. Covers every aspect of the subject, including an historical survey beginning before Linnaeus systematized nomenclature, the literal meaning of scores of Latin names, their English equivalents, etc. Enthusiastically written and easy to follow, this handbook for gardeners, amateur horticulturalists, and beginning botany students is knowledgeable, accurate and useful. 11 illustrations. Lists of Latin, English botanical names. 192pp. 5⅜ x 8½. T796 Paperbound **$1.15**

PIERRE CURIE, Marie Curie. Nobel Prize winner creates a memorable portrait of her equally famous husband in a fine scientific biography. Recounting his childhood, his haphazard education, and his experimental research (with his brother) in the physics of crystals, Mme. Curie brings to life the strong, determined personality of a great scientist at work and discusses, in clear, straightforward terms, her husband's and her own work with radium and radioactivity. A great book about two very great founders of modern science. Includes Mme. Curie's autobiographical notes. Translated by Charlotte and Vernon Kellogg. viii + 120pp. 5⅜ x 8½. T199 Paperbound **$1.00**

STYLES IN PAINTING: A Comparative Study, Paul Zucker. Professor of Art History at Cooper Union presents an important work of art-understanding that will guide you to a fuller, deeper appreciation of masterpieces of art and at the same time add to your understanding of how they fit into the evolution of style from the earliest times to this century. Discusses general principles of historical method and aesthetics, history of styles, then illustrates with more than 230 great paintings organized by subject matter so you can see at a glance how styles have changed through the centuries. 236 beautiful halftones. xiv + 338pp. 5⅝ x 8½. T760 Paperbound **$2.00**

NEW VARIORUM EDITION OF SHAKESPEARE
One of the monumental feats of Shakespeare scholarship is the famous New Variorum edition, containing full texts of the plays together with an entire reference library worth of historical and critical information: all the variant readings that appear in the quartos and folios; annotations by leading scholars from the earliest days of Shakespeare criticism to the date of publication; essays on meaning, background, productions by Johnson, Addison, Fielding, Lessing, Hazlitt, Coleridge, Ulrici, Swinburne, and other major Shakespeare critics; original sources of Shakespeare's inspiration. For the first time, this definitive edition of Shakespeare's plays, each printed in a separate volume, will be available in inexpensive editions to scholars, to teachers and students, and to every lover of Shakespeare and fine literature. Now ready:

KING LEAR, edited by Horace Howard Furness. Bibliography. List of editions collated in notes. viii + 503pp. 5⅜ x 8½. T1000 Paperbound **$2.25**

MACBETH, edited by Horace Howard Furness Jr. Bibliography. List of editions collated in notes. xvi + 562pp. 5⅜ x 8½. T1001 Paperbound **$2.25**

ROMEO AND JULIET, edited by Horace Howard Furness. Bibliography. List of editions collated in notes. xxvi + 480pp. 5⅜ x 8½. T1002 Paperbound **$2.25**

OTTHELLO, edited by Horace Howard Furness. Bibliography. List of editions collated in notes. x + 471pp. 5⅜ x 8½. T1003 Paperbound **$2.25**

HAMLET, edited by Horace Howard Furness. Bibliography. List of editions collated in notes. Total of 926pp. 5⅜ x 8½. T1004-1005 Two volume set, Paperbound **$4.50**

THE GARDENER'S YEAR, Karel Capek. The author of this refreshingly funny book is probably best known in U. S. as the author of "R. U. R.," a biting satire on the machine age. Here, his satiric genius finds expression in a wholly different vein: a warm, witty chronicle of the joys and trials of the amateur gardener as he watches over his plants, his soil and the weather from January to December. 59 drawings by Joseph Capek add an important second dimension to the fun. "Mr. Capek writes with sympathy, understanding and humor," NEW YORK TIMES. "Will delight the amateur gardener, and indeed everyone else," SATURDAY REVIEW. Translated by M. and R. Weatherall. 59 illustrations. 159pp. 4½ x 6½. T1014 Paperbound **$1.00**

THE ADVANCE OF THE FUNGI, E. C. Large. The dramatic story of the battle against fungi, from the year the potato blight hit Europe (1845) to 1940, and of men who fought and won it: Pasteur, Anton de Bary, Tulasne, Berkeley, Woronin, Jensen, many others. Combines remarkable grasp of facts and their significance with skill to write dramatic, exciting prose. "Philosophically witty, fundamentally thoughtful, always mature," NEW YORK HERALD TRIBUNE. "Highly entertaining, intelligent, penetrating," NEW YORKER. Bibliography. 64 illustrations. 6 full-page plates. 488pp. 5⅜ x 8½. T437 Paperbound **$2.25**

THE PAINTER'S METHODS AND MATERIALS, A. P. Laurie. Adviser to the British Royal Academy discusses the ills that paint is heir to and the methods most likely to counteract them. Examining 48 masterpieces by Fra Lippo Lippi, Millais, Boucher, Rembrandt, Romney, Van Eyck, Velazquez, Michaelangelo, Botticelli, Frans Hals, Turner, and others, he tries to discover how special and unique effects were achieved. Not conjectural information, but certain and authoritative. Beautiful, sharp reproductions, plus textual illustrations of apparatus and the results of experiments with pigments and media. 63 illustrations and diagrams. Index. 250pp. 5⅜ x 8. T1019 Clothbound **$3.75**

CHANCE, LUCK AND STATISTICS, H. C. Levinson. The theory of chance, or probability, and the science of statistics presented in simple, non-technical language. Covers fundamentals by analyzing games of chance, then applies those fundamentals to immigration and birth rates, operations research, stock speculation, insurance rates, advertising, and other fields. Excellent course supplement and a delightful introduction for non-mathematicians. Formerly "The Science of Chance." Index. xiv + 356pp. 5⅜ x 8. T1007 Paperbound **$1.85**

THROUGH THE ALIMENTARY CANAL WITH GUN AND CAMERA: A Fascinating Trip to the Interior, George S. Chappell. An intrepid explorer, better known as a major American humorist, accompanied by imaginary camera-man and botanist, conducts this unforgettably hilarious journey to the human interior. Wildly imaginative, his account satirizes academic pomposity, parodies cliché-ridden travel literature, and cleverly uses facts of physiology for comic purposes. All the original line drawings by Otto Soglow are included to add to the merriment. Preface by Robert Benchley. 17 illustrations. xii + 116pp. 5⅜ x 8½. T376 Paperbound **$1.00**

TALKS TO TEACHERS ON PSYCHOLOGY and to Students on Some of Life's Ideals, William James. America's greatest psychologist invests these lectures with immense personal charm, invaluable insights, and superb literary style. 15 Harvard lectures, 3 lectures delivered to students in New England touch upon psychology and the teaching of art, stream of consciousness, the child as a behaving organism, education and behavior, association of ideas, the gospel of relaxation, what makes life significant, and other related topics. Interesting, and still vital pedagogy. x + 146pp. 5⅜ x 8½. T261 Paperbound **$1.00**

A WHIMSEY ANTHOLOGY, collected by Carolyn Wells. Delightful verse on the lighter side: logical whimsies, poems shaped like decanters and flagons, lipograms and acrostics, alliterative verse, enigmas and charades, anagrams, linguistic and dialectic verse, tongue twisters, limericks, travesties, and just about very other kind of whimsical poetry ever written. Works by Edward Lear, Gelett Burgess, Poe, Lewis Carroll, Henley, Robert Herrick, Christina Rossetti, scores of other poets will entertain and amuse you for hours. Index. xiv + 221pp. 5⅜ x 8½. T1020 Paperbound **$1.25**

LANDSCAPE PAINTING, R. O. Dunlop. A distinguished modern artist is a perfect guide to the aspiring landscape painter. This practical book imparts to even the uninitiated valuable methods and techniques. Useful advice is interwoven throughout a fascinating illustrated history of landscape painting, from Ma Yüan to Picasso. 60 half-tone reproductions of works by Giotto, Giovanni Bellini, Piero della Francesca, Tintoretto, Giorgione, Raphael, Van Ruisdael, Poussin, Gainsborough, Monet, Cezanne, Seurat, Picasso, many others. Total of 71 illustrations, 4 in color. Index. 192pp. 7⅜ x 10. T1018 Clothbound **$6.00**

PRACTICAL LANDSCAPE PAINTING, Adrian Stokes. A complete course in landscape painting that trains the senses to perceive as well as the hand to apply the principles underlying the pictorial aspect of nature. Author fully explains tools, value and nature of various colors, and instructs beginners in clear, simple terms how to apply them. Places strong emphasis on drawing and composition, foundations often neglected in painting texts. Includes pictorial-textual survey of the art from Ancient China to the present, with helpful critical comments and numerous diagrams illustrating every stage. 93 illustrations. Index. 256pp. 5⅜ x 8. T1017 Clothbound **$3.75**

PELLUCIDAR, THREE NOVELS: AT THE EARTH'S CORE, PELLUCIDAR, TANAR OF PELLUCIDAR, Edgar Rice Burroughs. The first three novels of adventure in the thrill-filled world within the hollow interior of the earth. David Innes's mechanical mole drills through the outer crust and precipitates him into an astonishing world. Among Burroughs's most popular work. Illustrations by J. Allan St. John. 5⅜ x 8½. T1051 Paperbound **$2.00**
T1050 Clothbound **$3.75**

JOE MILLER'S JESTS OR, THE WITS VADE-MECUM. Facsimile of the first edition of famous 18th century collection of repartees, bons mots, puns and jokes, the father of the humor anthology. A first-hand look at the taste of fashionable London in the Age of Pope. 247 entertaining anecdotes, many involving well-known personages such as Colley Cibber, Sir Thomas More, Rabelais, rich in humor, historic interest. New introduction contains biographical information on Joe Miller, fascinating history of his enduring collection, bibliographical information on collections of comic material. Introduction by Robert Hutchinson. 96pp. 5⅜ x 8½. Paperbound **$1.00**

THE HUMOROUS WORLD OF JEROME K. JEROME. Complete essays and extensive passages from nine out-of-print books ("Three Men on Wheels," "Novel Notes," "Told After Supper," "Sketches in Lavender, Blue and Green," "American Wives and Others," 4 more) by a highly original humorist, author of the novel "Three Men in a Boat." Human nature is JKJ's subject: the problems of husbands, of wives, of tourists, of the human animal trapped in the drawing room. His sympathetic acceptance of the shortcomings of his race and his ability to see humor in almost any situation make this a treasure for those who know his work and a pleasant surprise for those who don't. Edited and with an introduction by Robert Hutchinson. xii + 260pp. 5⅜ x 8½. T58 Paperbound **$1.00**

GEOMETRY OF FOUR DIMENSIONS, H. P. Manning. Unique in English as a clear, concise introduction to this fascinating subject. Treatment is primarily synthetic and Euclidean, although hyperplanes and hyperspheres at infinity are considered by non-Euclidean forms. Historical introduction and foundations of 4-dimensional geometry; perpendicularity; simple angles; angles of planes; higher order; symmetry; order, motion; hyperpyramids, hypercones, hyperspheres; figures with parallel elements; volume, hypervolume in space; regular polyhedroids. Glossary of terms. 74 illustrations. ix + 348pp. 5⅜ x 8. S182 Paperbound **$2.00**

PAPER FOLDING FOR BEGINNERS, W. D. Murray and F. J. Rigney. A delightful introduction to the varied and entertaining Japanese art of origami (paper folding), with a full, crystal-clear text that anticipates every difficulty; over 275 clearly labeled diagrams of all important stages in creation. You get results at each stage, since complex figures are logically developed from simpler ones. 43 different pieces are explained: sailboats, frogs, roosters, etc. 6 photographic plates. 279 diagrams. 95pp. 5⅝ x 8⅜. T713 Paperbound **$1.00**

SATELLITES AND SCIENTIFIC RESEARCH, D. King-Hele. An up-to-the-minute non-technical account of the man-made satellites and the discoveries they have yielded up to September of 1961. Brings together information hitherto published only in hard-to-get scientific journals. Includes the life history of a typical satellite, methods of tracking, new information on the shape of the earth, zones of radiation, etc. Over 60 diagrams and 6 photographs. Mathematical appendix. Bibliography of over 100 items. Index. xii + 180pp. 5⅜ x 8½. T703 Paperbound **$2.00**

LOUIS PASTEUR, S. J. Holmes. A brief, very clear, and warmly understanding biography of the great French scientist by a former Professor of Zoology in the University of California. Traces his home life, the fortunate effects of his education, his early researches and first theses, and his constant struggle with superstition and institutionalism in his work on microorganisms, fermentation, anthrax, rabies, etc. New preface by the author. 159pp. 5⅜ x 8. T197 Paperbound **$1.00**

THE ENJOYMENT OF CHESS PROBLEMS, K. S. Howard. A classic treatise on this minor art by an internationally recognized authority that gives a basic knowledge of terms and themes for the everyday chess player as well as the problem fan: 7 chapters on the two-mover; 7 more on 3- and 4-move problems; a chapter on selfmates; and much more. "The most important one-volume contribution originating solely in the U.S.A.," Alain White. 200 diagrams. Index. Solutions, viii + 212pp. 5⅜ x 8. T742 Paperbound **$1.25**

SAM LOYD AND HIS CHESS PROBLEMS, Alain C. White. Loyd was (for all practical purposes) the father of the American chess problem and his protégé and successor presents here the diamonds of his production, chess problems embodying a whimsy and bizarre fancy entirely unique. More than 725 in all, ranging from two-move to extremely elaborate five-movers, including Loyd's contributions to chess oddities—problems in which pieces are arranged to form initials, figures, other by-paths of chess problem found nowhere else. Classified according to major concept, with full text analyzing problems, containing selections from Loyd's own writings. A classic to challenge your ingenuity, increase your skill. Corrected republication of 1913 edition. Over 750 diagrams and illustrations. 744 problems with solutions. 471pp. 5⅜ x 8½. T928 Paperbound **$2.25**

FABLES IN SLANG & MORE FABLES IN SLANG, George Ade. 2 complete books of major American humorist in pungent colloquial tradition of Twain, Billings. 1st reprinting in over 30 years includes "The Two Mandolin Players and the Willing Performer," "The Base Ball Fan Who Took the Only Known Cure," "The Slim Girl Who Tried to Keep a Date that was Never Made," 42 other tales of eccentric, perverse, but always funny characters. "Touch of genius," H. L. Mencken. New introduction by E. F. Bleiler. 86 illus. 208pp. 5⅜ x 8. T533 Paperbound **$1.00**

Prices subject to change without notice.

Dover publishes books on art, music, philosophy, literature, languages, history, social sciences, psychology, handcrafts, orientalia, puzzles and entertainments, chess, pets and gardens, books explaining science, intermediate and higher mathematics, mathematical physics, engineering, biological sciences, earth sciences, classics of science, etc. Write to:

Dept. catrr.
Dover Publications, Inc.
180 Varick Street, N.Y. 14, N.Y.